# Connect to
# NCTM Standards 2000

## Making the Standards
## Work at Kindergarten

Francis (Skip) Fennell, Ph.D.

Honi J. Bamberger, Ph.D.

Thomas E. Rowan, Ph.D.

Kay B. Sammons

Anna R. Suarez

Creative Publications®
A Tribune Education Company

## Acknowledgments

**Project Editors** → Diane Nieker, Jeff Stiegel

**Writers** → Tim Burnett, Marilyn Davis, Beth Sycamore

**Writing and Editorial Services** → MathLink, Inc.

**Design Director** → Karen Stack

**Design** → Gerta Sorensen-London

**Project Coordinator** → Barbara Quincer

**Cover Illustration** → Jim Dandy

**Illustrators** → Susan Aiello, Jim Dandy, Sarah Frederking

**Production** → Inkwell Publishing Solutions, Inc

**Manufacturing** → Dallas Richards

© 2000 Creative Publications®, Inc.

Two Prudential Plaza

Chicago, IL 60601

This is an independent publication and is not affiliated with, or sponsored by, the NCTM. The NCTM 2000 Standards are not reproduced in this book. This book is designed to be read independently of the *Principles and Standards for School Mathematics* and to aid educators in preparing to teach in a manner consistent with the *Principles and Standards*.

ISBN 0-7622-1242-x

Catalog No. 21008

Customer Service 800-624-0822

http://www.creativepublications.com

1 2 3 4 5 6 7 8 MAL 05 04 03 02 01 00

BK
$24.45

# Contents

# Overview

Since *Curriculum and Evaluation Standards for School Mathematics* was released in 1989, much has been learned about how ideas work in the classroom and how children learn mathematics. The release of the *Principles and Standards for School Mathematics* creates an opportunity for us to examine our goals, our math curricula, and our teaching methods in light of these new insights and to consider practices and procedures that will improve school mathematics education. As did the original draft, *Principles and Standards* promotes ways for all educators to strengthen the teaching and learning of mathematics by addressing two important concerns: the characteristics of instructional programs that will provide high-quality mathematical experiences for children as they progress through school, and the mathematical content and processes children should know and use as they advance from grade to grade.

## General Overview

*Connect to NCTM Standards 2000* is designed to help you understand and implement the NCTM standards. Regardless of your teaching style, the information presented in this book will help you to make the standards work. *Principles and Standards* identifies ten standards. Five of those standards are described as content standards that organize all of mathematics into five broad areas of learning; they address *what* children learn. The other five standards, the process standards, are concerned with *how* children learn and how information is presented.

Today, more than ever, there is a need for all children to have a strong base in mathematics. This means that children do not just memorize facts and procedures, but that they have an understanding of mathematics and mathematical thinking. The interplay between content and process is complicated, but integrating the two is critical if our children are to receive the mathematics education they will need to function effectively in the world they will grow into.

The lessons contained within *Connect to NCTM Standards 2000* are organized into sections by content. Each section contains four lessons dealing with some aspect of that content standard. Each lesson demonstrates ways to develop the content by using the process standards. An overview highlights grade-level content skills and gives a brief description of the four lessons for that standard.

---

**Content Standards**

Number and Operation

Algebra

Geometry

Measurement

Data Analysis and Probability

---

**Process Standards**

Problem Solving

Reasoning and Proof

Communication

Connections

Representation

The last section of the book, entitled Create Your Own Lesson, is designed to help you develop lessons of your own that will comfortably incorporate the NCTM standards with your teaching style.

## About the Lessons

Each content standard section contains four lessons that address some aspect of the content at the grade level. Three of the lessons have been specially developed to model ways the process standards can be used to develop the content being presented. The fourth lesson examines a hypothetical math textbook lesson in terms of how the process standards are incorporated into that lesson. Suggestions are offered for increasing the focus on three of the five process standards to create a more effective lesson. Then, a lesson is presented modeling how those suggestions can be implemented.

As you read through the lessons, keep in mind that what is offered is only one possible approach. You might have a completely different idea about how to develop the concept, and that's fine. These lessons are intended to provide examples of how the process standards can work to make mathematics lessons more meaningful, and to model questions and techniques that you might incorporate into your teaching. As you read through the lessons, pay attention to how the process standards are being used. Use the ideas presented as a springboard for your own ideas.

Each lesson is intended for a single class period. Some introduce a concept, others require that children have some experience with the concept, and still others are meant to be used at the end of a unit. As you examine these lessons, think about how and where they fit into your curriculum. Any of the lessons here can be used as a replacement for the comparable lesson in your current math program. Try the lessons and see the difference incorporating the process standards can make.

## Creating Your Own Lessons

The last section of the book is designed to help you develop lessons of your own that incorporate the NCTM standards and are compatible with your teaching style. You will find questions to help you focus on ideas to consider as you begin to organize a standards-based lesson. You will also have an opportunity to follow the thoughts and decisions one person used in the process of developing a lesson.

# About the Authors

## Francis (Skip) Fennell, Ph.D.

Dr. Fennell was a member of the writing team of *Principles and Standards for School Mathematics* (NCTM, 2000). He has authored mathematics textbooks, materials for both children and teachers, and numerous articles for leading mathematics journals. Dr. Fennell has served on the Board of Directors of NCTM and as Program Officer of instructional materials and teacher enhancement within the Division of Elementary, Secondary, and Informal Education at the National Science Foundation. He has been selected as Outstanding Mathematics Educator by the Maryland Council of Teachers of Mathematics, and as Professor of the Year by both the Carnegie Foundation and Western Maryland College, where he is a professor of education.

## Honi J. Bamberger, Ph.D.

Dr. Bamberger is a recognized math scholar and teacher. She has taught at both the elementary school and college levels, served as an associate research scientist and mathematics consultant for Johns Hopkins University, and contributed as a consultant and content writer for the "Numbers Alive" public television series. Dr. Bamberger has presented her research findings at mathematics conferences across the country, and has been an author for a number of mathematics textbooks. Currently, Dr. Bamberger is executive director of Insight, a consulting firm specializing in professional development in mathematics education.

### Thomas E. Rowan, Ph.D.

Dr. Rowan was a member of the working group that wrote the K–4 section of the *Curriculum and Evaluation Standards for School Mathematics*. Since the Standards were first published, he has worked with many school systems to help bring about the transition to standards-based classroom mathematics instruction in grades K–8. Dr. Rowan is a frequent presenter at NCTM and author of mathematics texts and numerous articles on teaching and learning mathematics. He currently teaches at the University of Maryland where he focuses on methods of teaching elementary school mathematics.

### Kay B. Sammons

Kay Sammons is currently Elementary Mathematics Supervisor for the Howard County Public Schools in Ellicott City, Maryland, where she is responsible for curriculum and staff development for elementary teachers. She is a frequent presenter at state and national mathematics conferences. In addition to serving as a reviewer for NCTM publications, she has written textbooks and teacher resource materials. Ms. Sammons was honored as Elementary Mathematics Teacher of the Year by the Maryland Council Teachers of Mathematics and as Outstanding Educator of the Year by that same organization.

### Anna R. Suarez

Anna Suarez is a national consultant and program director for K–8 Mathematics at the National Science Foundation in Arlington, Virginia. Her participation in an NSF-funded research study, Cognitively Guided Instruction (C.G.I.), helped to develop teachers' knowledge of children's mathematical thinking as the basis for making instructional decisions. She has written staff development materials for both the *Investigations* curriculum and Insight.

# About the Standards

*T*he *Principles and Standards for School Mathematics 2000* are built around ten curriculum standards. Five of those standards address the mathematical content, or body of mathematical knowledge, that children should learn. Content standards prescribe *what* is to be taught in mathematics. The content standards are Number and Operation, Algebra, Geometry, Measurement, and Data Analysis and Probability.

The other five standards are process standards. The process standards describe *how* the content is delivered. They address how children will acquire the necessary mathematical content and how that knowledge will be applied. The five process standards are identified as Problem Solving, Reasoning and Proof, Communication, Connections, and Representation.

It should be pointed out that the content standards and process standards are not separate subsets of the whole, but are intricately interrelated. How mathematics is learned is as important as what mathematics is learned. The process standards help to "frame" how the content standards are presented.

It is possible to weave the process standards into the teaching of mathematics through a variety of methods. Children can and should be presented with meaningful problems to solve and situations that require them to reason through information to find solutions. They should be asked to defend their solutions and explain their thinking. In presenting a problem to children, connections might be made to a similar problem to build on previous learning. A representative model might be used to enhance children's understanding of a concept. Continuous communication, written and oral, will provide feedback about children's understanding.

For children to become mathematically powerful, it is essential that they be able to use process skills flexibly. They need to practice applying reasoning to solve problems and proving that their solutions are correct. They need to experiment with a variety of representations and have the ability to use them in solving problems and in illustrating their thinking. They should be able to communicate their mathematical thinking and solutions to the teacher and to other children both orally and in writing. Making connections between problems within mathematics is as essential as is making mathematical connections to disciplines outside of mathematics. The importance of how these processes interrelate and work together cannot be overemphasized.

------------------------------------

**Content Standards**

**Number and Operation**

**Algebra**

**Geometry**

**Measurement**

**Data Analysis and Probability**

------------------------------------

**Process Standards**

**Problem Solving**

**Reasoning and Proof**

**Communication**

**Connections**

**Representation**

## Primary Problem Solving

**P**ROBLEM SOLVING IS AT THE HEART of mathematics—it is what mathematicians do. Balance is achieved through the interrelationship of conceptual learning, basic skills, and problem solving. Developing concepts with concrete representations ensures understanding and enables students to create a strong foundation on which to build. Children need basic skills in order to apply and record their understandings with efficiency. But most importantly, they need good problems to solve, problems in which they can apply their conceptual understanding and utilize basic skills.

In its simplest form, problem solving means finding a solution when the answer is not readily apparent. Because problem solving does not always follow a uniform plan, children need to develop persistence to be able to work problems through to the end. Sometimes persistence means changing direction. *Well, we know that way doesn't work. What should we try next? Is there another way we can look at this problem?* Questions that encourage children to look for other options should be an integral part of the discussions that take place in mathematics classes.

Choosing problems that have relevance to children is an important factor in creating enthusiasm for problem solving. Often, the enthusiasm of the teacher translates into a positive disposition toward problem solving for children. If statements like "Now that's an unusual problem. I wonder how we can find the answer," are part of a teacher's repertoire, children get the notion that problem solving is interesting and they are encouraged to use their own resources to find a path to the solution.

Acquiring a variety of strategies to access for problem solving is essential to experiencing success. Having flexibility to solve problems in different ways enables children to get "unstuck" if they reach a "dead end;" it allows them to have other approaches to try. Children should be provided with instruction and practice in using a wide range of strategies that they can then draw upon.

Many young children come to school with an innate understanding of how to solve mathematical problems. The teachers' task is to build on this problem-solving ability by posing challenging problems that are accessible to all children. Fortunately, the primary classroom is full of wonderful problems for young children.

Asking thought-provoking questions to help children begin and sustain the process of solving the problem is another important role of the teacher.

- *How many days are there until Halloween? How can we find out?*

- *If we divide the class into three teams, how many children will be on each team? What can we do that will help us figure this out?*

- *If everyone gets four crackers, how many crackers will we need altogether? If a box contains 24 crackers, will one box be enough? How many boxes will we need?*

- *If we want to extend our pattern, what shape should come next? How can we find out?*

Children should be encouraged to talk with one another and share their thinking with each other as well as the teacher as they solve problems. "Two heads are better than one" is an old saying that has special meaning in the process

of problem solving. As children work together, they are able to come up with many more approaches to a problem than a child working alone would. The teacher should point out differing strategies for the solution of a problem. Children should be asked to compare the strategies to see if there are similarities and note how they differ. Children should also be asked to consider which solutions they think work best for the particular problem and why. This opens the door to a rich discussion that will broaden the learning experience for all.

## Primary Reasoning and Proof

REASONING IS FUNDAMENTAL TO THE STUDY of mathematics— it is a state of mind that causes children to explore, to justify, and to validate. It permeates all content areas and all grade levels. Children are reasoning when they interpret data, when they solve problems, and when they view geometric patterns and shapes. As they are presented with new problems, they use reasoning skills to apply previously acquired information and to test the validity of their solutions. Reasoning is the process by which children make sense of mathematics.

As they develop mathematically, children learn that mathematics is a discipline based on an inherent set of rules. Reasoning begins with intuition. This

intuition is used by even the youngest children in their efforts to make sense of mathematics, and it should be encouraged as the basis of reasoning at all grade levels. This informal intuition will become the basis for reasoning through representations that are more formal and for proofs based upon the rules.

Activities that have children compare, sort, and classify provide wonderful opportunities to develop reasoning skills. In a kindergarten classroom, children might use the buttons in a button jar and sort them by a variety of attributes. One child might place all the buttons of one color together; another might sort the buttons by the number of holes; still another by the material from which they're made, such as metal, plastic, or wood. The reasoning at this age is generally limited to one attribute. But as a child advances to first and second grade, he may be able to sort the buttons by two attributes to make a set that includes only buttons that are red and have four holes. When children explain their rules for sorting and how their choices were made, they are able to validate their thinking.

Being able to identify patterns is another prerequisite for the development of reasoning skills. A child who can recognize that the pattern is 2 hearts and 3 stars will be able to extend the pattern and to predict what shape will come next.

♥♥★★★♥♥★★★

What are some other ways reasoning and proof can be incorporated into the mathematics class? An excellent way is by asking questions. *How did you get your answer? Tell me how you thought about that? Why does your solution work?* Questions such as these help children learn that it is important to have reasons for what they say. They also help children realize that mathematics makes sense and isn't just a system of rules and procedures to be blindly followed.

Another powerful way to develop reasoning in young children is to engage them in mathematical discussions. Piaget believed that in order for children to develop reasoning, it was imperative to have social interaction. Designating time during the mathematics lesson for discussion about their thinking allows that interaction. In any class, there will be a wide range of reasoning ability; it's helpful for children with less mature reasoning abilities to hear from those with well-developed skills. Mathematical discussions increase a child's repertoire of reasoning skills.

In a first grade class, the teacher might ask children to give the sum of 8 + 7. When called upon, a child responds with the sum and is asked to explain how the sum was found.

- One child might explain that he got the answer by counting on his fingers and demonstrate that by physically counting eight fingers and then adding seven more.

- Another child may draw tally marks on paper to represent 8 and 7 and then show that it is equal to 15 by counting to eight and then counting on from there to fifteen.

- Another child might tell you that she knows $8 + 7 = 15$ because she can "take the two out of seven and combine it with the eight to make 10. There is 5 left over so 10 and 5 make fifteen. $8 + 7 = 8 + (2 + 5) = 10 + 5 = 15$."

- Still another student might say, "I know that $7 + 7 = 14$ and 1 more is 15."

All of these children are using what they know is true about mathematics and using mathematical reasoning to solve the problem. A child who is still counting on his fingers to get that answer will hear strategies from other children that he can begin to think about and later apply.

Working on reasoning skills and having children offer explanations of their thinking to defend their answers in the primary grades helps lay the foundation for more formal mathematical argumentation in later grades.

## Primary Communication

WHETHER BETWEEN TEACHER AND CHILD, between a pair of children, or among groups of children, the communication skills of reading, writing, and listening and speaking provide the means for sharing ideas and promoting mathematical understanding. As children express their ideas through oral and written language, they have an opportunity to clarify their thinking and reinforce their own comprehension of concepts they are working with. By listening to explanations given by their classmates, children are exposed to ideas they may not have thought of. This provides a greater network of connections among ideas and, in turn, enhances learning.

Ample opportunities to discuss mathematical ideas should be provided. One extremely effective technique that was described in the previous section on Reasoning and Proof involves presenting an interesting problem to the class, allowing time to solve the problem, and then asking children to explain how they solved the problem. Providing a forum for a number of different solutions to be presented and defended by children results in rich dialogue.

There is a very high level of mental activity associated with social interaction of this nature. Children who are afforded opportunities to take part in these mathematical conversations on a regular basis learn more effectively how to reason and defend their answers. In the process, they also learn to communicate and to clarify and refine their ideas, which leads to deeper understanding.

Through discussion, children also learn to organize their mathematical thinking in order to communicate their ideas to one another. In their exchange of ideas, children naturally want to have their position make sense. Providing opportunities to present their views allows young children to articulate, clarify, organize, and consolidate their thinking. This communication enables them to reflect on what they know and demonstrate this knowledge to others.

When children are able to articulate their ideas the teacher gains insight into their thinking. For example, one kindergarten child told a teacher that he knew 5 + 2 = 8. Because the child was able to verbalize the idea, the teacher was able to help the child modify the answer by asking him to prove the

answer using objects like Teddy Bear Counters. As the child counted 5 and 2 more, he realized that he only had 7, not 8.

Astounding language development is characteristic of the primary grades. It is important at this level that children begin to understand and use the special language of mathematics. Every opportunity to build conventional mathematical vocabulary should be taken advantage of. For example, during playtime as a child explains a shape to his friend and describes it as "the one with 4 sides," there's an opportunity for the teacher to explain that the shape is a *square*.

Putting ideas on paper also helps young children organize their thinking. The act of writing something down causes students to organize ideas and refine them before committing them to paper. Words, pictures, and numbers are all part of written communication. Journal writing, which can begin in kindergarten, helps children relate what they know about mathematics and can serve as an important tool for teachers as they assess their children's mathematical understanding.

Primary grade children should be provided with opportunities to share their mathematical ideas on a daily basis. This process is essential to internalizing mathematics.

## Primary Connections

MAKING CONNECTIONS IN MATHEMATICS is a three-fold process. Connections are made when one mathematical idea is used to build another; they are made among different mathematical ideas and content areas; and they are made between mathematics and contexts outside the field of mathematics.

Because mathematics is an integrated discipline, treating it as a whole body of knowledge and focusing on the connections that occur naturally adds dimension to ideas and concepts. How is counting related to addition, addition to subtraction, addition to multiplication, multiplication to area? A cohesive curriculum that is clearly articulated from pre-kindergarten through the twelfth grade, one that connects the mathematical ideas within each grade as well as the mathematics between grade levels, is critical if those connections are to take place.

Making connections to prior mathematical experiences is vital for the understanding of how mathematical ideas build on one another. Teachers need to know what mathematics children learned previously in order to build on that knowledge. In a given unit of study, attention should be paid to ensure that mathematics concepts build upon one another from day to day in a coherent manner. Teachers should also be aware of what their children will be studying in subsequent grades so they can lay the foundation for obvious connections to further studies.

Mathematics permeates other curriculum areas and it is found in the everyday experience outside of school as well. The use of shapes and patterns is prevalent in art and architecture; measurement skills and classification skills are important in science; measurement skills and knowledge of fractions are utilized in cooking and in building models; and measurement skills, data gathering, and statistics are applied in the social sciences.

Because mathematics is often integrated into other subjects at the primary level, the children do not view it as a separate study. They count the number of boys and girls in attendance at school each day. They look for patterns on the calendar and in the environment. They build with blocks, observing and communicating about the attributes of each. They sort and classify a variety of objects. They plant seeds and measure their growth.

As young children strive to make sense of their world, they naturally make connections to prior experiences. As a pre-schooler counts a group of four juice boxes on the table and says, "One, two, three, four," counting numbers are being connected with objects. The counting may be based on hearing someone else count, or the child may have had previous counting experiences and is able to transfer those experiences to this new situation. Many pre-school children are not able to recite a counting number for each object they point to because they have not yet internalized one-to-one correspondence. They don't yet understand that if they count each object and end up at 4, there are 4 objects in the group. How are such connections made? Repeated experiences in the classroom where children have opportunities to count boys, girls, crayons, blocks, and so on, will ensure those connections over time.

It is important for teachers to be conscious of connections that can be made in mathematics and to weave those connections into daily practice. When children are able to connect mathematical ideas both inside and outside of the classroom, they begin to see mathematics as a cohesive body of knowledge.

## Primary Representation

REPRESENTATIONS PROVIDE VEHICLES for expressing and internalizing mathematical thought. They are a critical component in shaping the way children access, understand, express, and utilize mathematical ideas. Representations include physical objects, pictures, and symbols. They also include mental images, words, and ideas.

Representations can be formal or informal. Examples of formal representations are the conventional symbols, graphs, diagrams, and so on traditionally introduced in school mathematics. More informal forms are often invented by children as a way of making sense of mathematical ideas and communicating

those ideas to classmates or the teacher. Children should be allowed to create their own understanding and explanations, and to express relationships before more conventional representations are introduced. Connecting to their invented forms will facilitate a meaningful transition to thinking and communicating in the language of mathematics.

As teachers design lessons, choosing the type of representations they feel will best help children understand a concept becomes an important consideration. What shared mathematical language is needed to effectively communicate ideas? What manipulatives or models will be appropriate? How will children record their understanding of the concept? When is it appropriate to move from physical to symbolic representation?

Consider this problem for kindergarten children.

**A man went fishing in the morning and caught 3 fish. In the afternoon, he caught 4 more fish. How many did he catch all together?**

A kindergarten child might use counters representing the situation to help make sense of the problem.

The teacher must decide when it's appropriate to move to a more formal representation of the information. By the time that child reaches second grade, there should be no difficulty representing that same problem symbolically.

$$3 + 4 = 7$$

There are multiple representations for any mathematics concept. The greater the number of ways to represent the same idea a child has knowledge of, the greater the flexibility available in solving problems. For example, the number 25 can be thought of as 2 tens and 5 ones; the same as a quarter; halfway between 1 and 50; an odd number; one more than 24; five less than 30; 12 + 13; and so on. A child with access to this variety of representations of 25 is able to choose which version is useful for a particular situation.

One way to successfully build multiple representations for a number with young children is to feature a number each day in the classroom. Begin the math period by presenting a number for the day, such as 18, and ask children to find as many ways as they can to make that number. This activity is one that all children can work on, and it will increase their ability to think flexibly. Here are some names for 18 found by a second grader.

| | | |
|---|---|---|
| $18 + 0$ | $17 + 1$ | $9 + 9$ |
| $16 + 2$ | $9 \times 2$ | $20 - 2$ |
| $6 + 6 + 6$ | $10 + 8$ | $22 - 4$ |
| $5 + 5 + 5 + 3$ | $10 + 10 - 2$ | $9 + 8 + 1$ |
| $1+1+1+1+1+1+1+1+1+1+1+1+1+1+1+1+1+1$ | | |

To begin with, children record their mathematical ideas in very personal ways. As they continue their mathematical growth, they are introduced to conventional representations. Both forms of representation are powerful tools for understanding and communicating abstract ideas.

## Conclusion

The process standards are not an end in, and of, themselves. Rather, they provide the advanced organizers or plan for lessons that present important mathematics content. Seeing connections among mathematical topics enables children to reason and make sense of new ideas and problem-solving situations they encounter. Through the process of communication, children are able to represent these new ideas either formally or informally.

Just as the process standards are interrelated, so are the process and content standards. For true mathematical thinking and learning to occur, both process and content need to be skillfully woven into and through each lesson. That is the goal to work toward.

# Standard 1 **Number and Operation**

**A**T THE KINDERGARTEN LEVEL, number and operation includes children relating the numeral, written word, and dot pattern representations of the single-digit numbers, developing a sense of just how many objects are represented by each single-digit number, and understanding the concepts of one more and one less. Our lessons are derived from these important topics, and include a lesson on relating the numerals 1 through 6 with their respective dot patterns, a lesson that reinforces the understanding of one more or one less, a lesson that connects the numerals 1 through 6 with their respective written-word names, and a lesson that develops a sense of the magnitude of the number 5.

Three lessons model how the process standards can be used to teach content. A fourth lesson is a hypothetical textbook lesson that we have revised to be more standards based. These four lessons do not represent the entire curriculum, but rather provide glimpses of how, with a more concentrated effort to incorporate the process standards, better mathematics teaching and learning can be achieved.

One lesson we have chosen relates the numerals 1 through 6 with their respective dot patterns. Through many opportunities for communication about the dot patterns and how to recognize how many dots are in each pattern, children will be able to make the connections between the different representations of the six numbers.

Another lesson we have chosen is one that develops the concepts of one more and one less. Connections is the process standard that propels this lesson, as children relate phrases that they hear with whether the phrase indicates one more or one less. Children also connect one more and one less to their counting

A third lesson we have chosen suggests one strategy for adding three numbers—to look for a pair of numbers that add to 10, then add the third number. The process standard of reasoning and proof propels this lesson. Children write the six ways in which three addends may be added, notice that the sum is always the same, and decide which of the ways was the easiest or most efficient.

The hypothetical textbook lesson that we have chosen to revise has children recognize, identify, and create groups of five. Through the process standards of representation and connections, and communication children engage in a broad range of activities that build and extend their awareness of five.

## Standard 1 Lessons

-------------------------------------------
**Connecting Numeral and
Dot Patterns**
-------------------------------------------
**Determining One More,
One Less**
-------------------------------------------
**Linking Numerals and
Number Words**
-------------------------------------------
**Developing Number Sense:
Groups of Five**

# Connecting Numerals and Dot Patterns

## Introduction

**Objective** → Children will use visual dot patterns to understand the quantities represented by the numerals 1 through 6 without using one-to-one counting.

**Context** → Children have counted groups of objects and have also written some of the numbers these groups represent. They will continue to learn to represent numbers in a variety of ways and combinations.

## NCTM Standards Focus

The emphasis of this lesson is to help children recognize and visualize dot patterns. Rather than just memorizing patterns as is done in many lessons, children develop strategies for using and applying patterns. By focusing on the two process standards of connections and communication, children internalize their own strategies for determining the quantity each dot pattern represents. They begin to use an inventory of patterns that represent quantity rather than rely on one-to-one counting for small numbers.

**Connections** Children make connections between the visual patterns and the quantity a number represents.

**Communication** Children discuss how recognizing patterns of dots helps them figure out the quantity the dots represent. They share their thoughts with partners and with the class and they evaluate the thoughts of their classmates.

## Teaching Plan

**Materials** → Student pages 22–23; number cubes with dots; scissors

BEGIN THE LESSON BY SHOWING children a number cube. Count the number of dots on each face with them. Assign children partners and give each pair a number cube with dots.

Explain that one child will toss the number cube and the other will tell how many dots as quickly as possible. Model how to play the game by playing it with one child while the rest of the class watches. Toss the number cube and have the child tell the number of dots showing. Count the dots aloud to verify that the number the child said is correct. Then let the child toss the number cube while you tell the number. Have the child check your answer. Take turns doing this until you are sure that children understand the game.

After children have played for a short while, bring them together. *How does learning to recognize the patterns of dots on the cube make it easier and faster to figure out the number the dots represent?* Have children explain how recognizing the pattern that represents a number helped them to identify the number quickly. This will give children an excellent opportunity to communicate on two levels. First, they will communicate their own strategies and thinking. Second, they will listen to and evaluate the thinking of their classmates and incorporate these strategies into their own thinking. Ask volunteers to tell about how they determined the quantity each dot pattern represents.

### Methods Children Might Use

- They might look at the lines the dots form. For example, a diagonal line is 2 if the dots are far apart or 3 if the dots are closer together.

- They might look at the shapes the dots form. For example, if there is a dot in each corner the number is 4, because the face of the cube is a square.

- They might evaluate the quantity, so that if there are a lot of dots, the number is probably 5 or 6.

- They might look at the combinations of dots. For example, if there is a dot in each corner and one in the middle, the number is 5 because 4 and 1 is 5.

HAVE CHILDREN RETURN TO THE GAME. Observe whether children are trying to recognize the patterns the class discussed rather than trying to count the dots. When one partner has said how many dots are showing, the other partner looks at the pattern and either agrees or disagrees. If the children disagree, they can count the number of dots to determine who has the correct answer.

After a few minutes, change the activity slightly. Give children student page 22 and have them cut out the numeral cards 1 through 6. Then tell them to continue the activity in the same way except that, instead of saying the number, they are to choose the numeral that represents the quantity. Have one child toss the number cube. The other child picks out the numeral that represents the number of dots. Children alternate roles after a few turns.

## Extension

Use two number cubes. Have one child toss both cubes and the other child say how many dots are on each number cube.

The following activities work well with small groups or as math center activities.

**Activity 1: Different dots, same number.** Make different dot formations for the same number using paper plates and self-adhesive stick-on dots. Have children match the different representations of each number and copy them onto a piece of paper. Encourage them to keep all of the patterns for each number on a separate piece of paper.

**Activity 2: Domino match.** Give children several index cards and enough self-adhesive stick-on dots. Have them fold the cards in half and trace the fold line. Ask them to create domino cards by making different dot patterns for the numbers 1 through 6 on each side of each card. They should create at least three patterns for each number and should not use the same dot pattern more than once. Have children play dominoes in pairs. Encourage them to place dominoes with different patterns next to each other.

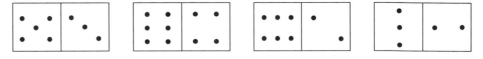

**Activity 3: Dot patterns.** Have children use counters and a sheet of paper. They make a pattern representing each number from 1 through 6 using the counters. They then trace or copy the patterns they made and write the numeral below each pattern.

**Activity 4: Patterns for greater numbers.** Give children paper plates and self-adhesive stick-on dots. Encourage them to make dot patterns for the numbers 7 through 10.

**Activity 5: Dot pattern chart.** Draw 6 rows of 7 boxes on a poster board. Write the numerals 1 through 6 in the first box of each row. Have children take turns showing different dot patterns in the squares.

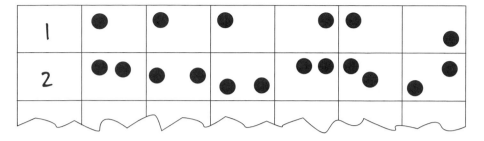

## Student Pages

Student page 22 has the numerals from 1 through 6 printed in rectangular boxes for children to cut out and use as number cards. Student page 23 has several dot patterns. The children write the numeral that matches these patterns. Read the directions aloud to the children before they work on the exercises.

## Assessment

The activities in this lesson gave you the opportunity to observe the processes by which the children learned to recognize dot patterns and associate them with numerals and quantity. As children discussed their strategies with each other and with you, you could assess how well they were integrating pattern recognition into their knowledge and skills base. As you review your observations during the lesson, consider whether the children have begun to develop and use an inventory of patterns that represent quantity rather than using one-to-one counting for small numbers.

## NCTM Standards Summary

In this lesson, children made connections between visual patterns and the corresponding numerals and quantities that the patterns represent. They also matched the patterns with the appropriate written numerals. They discussed how the patterns of dots helped them recognize the quantity the dots represented. They communicated their thoughts and strategies in whole class discussion and evaluated the thoughts and strategies of their classmates. They may have incorporated some of their classmates' strategies into their thinking. They then had an opportunity to apply their revised strategies as they repeated the initial activity of the lesson.

**Answers**

*Page 23*
1. 6
2. 4
3. 5
4. 3
5. 1
6. 2

# Connecting Numerals and Dot Patterns

**Cut out each number card.**

**Standard 1** Number and Operation

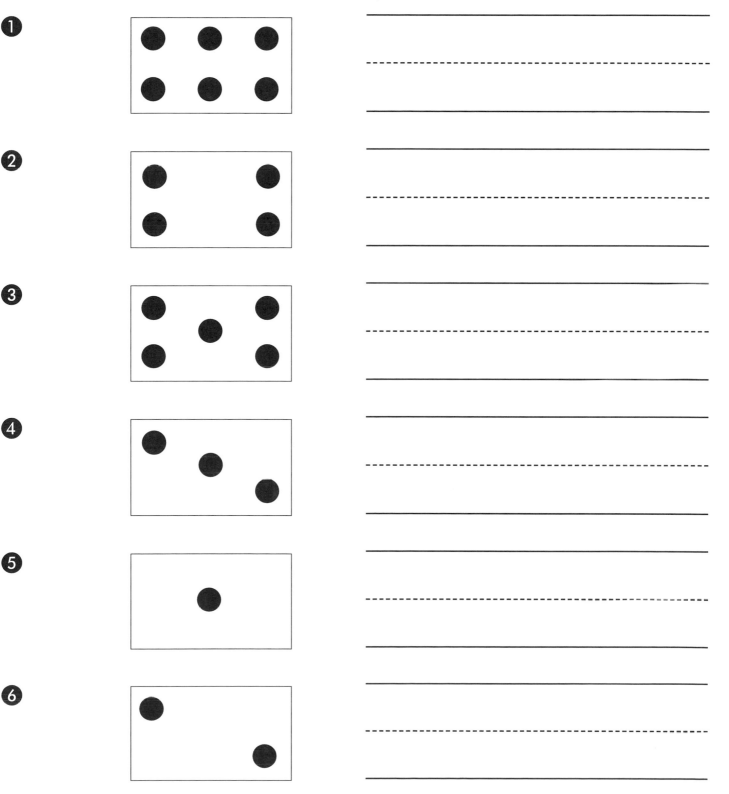

Name

## Connecting Numerals and Dot Patterns

**Write the numeral that matches each dot pattern.**

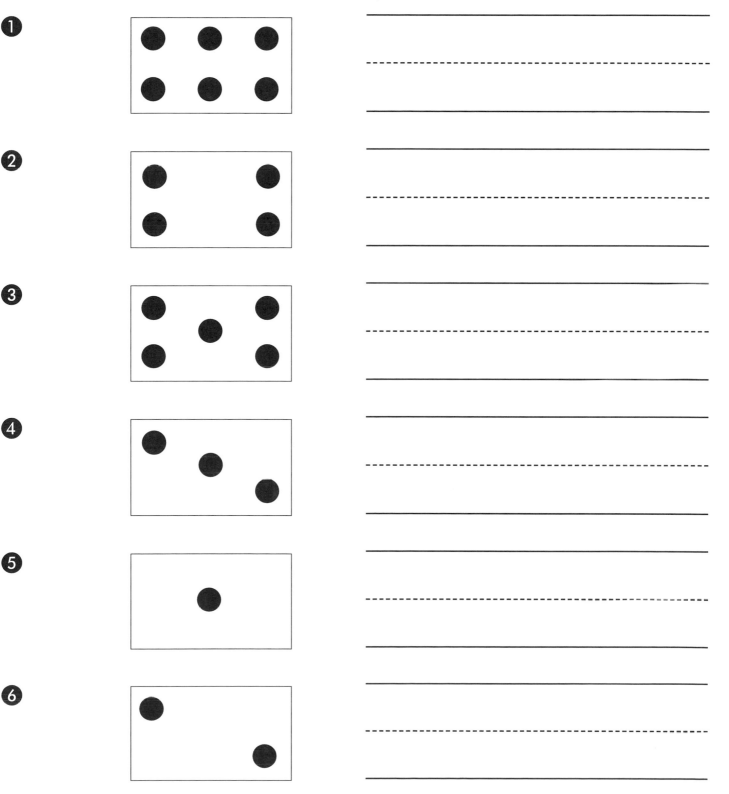

Standard 1 Number and Operation

Name

## Connecting Numerals and Dot Patterns

**Write the numeral that matches each dot pattern.**

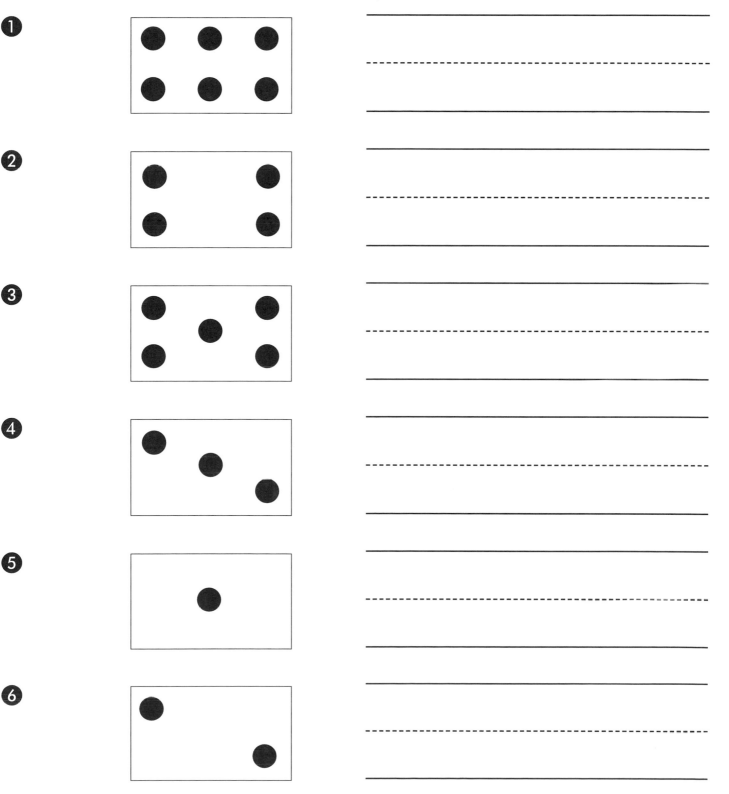

1.

2.

3.

4.

5.

6.

Standard 1 Number and Operation

Connect to NCTM Standards Kindergarten → 23

# Determining One More, One Less

## Introduction

-------------------------------------

**Objective** → Children will understand the concept of one more or one less. They will identify the relationships between numbers that are one more or one less than a given number.

**Context** → Children are able to count forward from 1 to 10 and back from 10 to 1. They will continue to explore number relationships by working with numbers that are two more or two less than a given number.

## NCTM Standards Focus

In this standards-based lesson, children pursue an investigatory approach to the concepts of "more" and "less." They develop their own methods for determining whether a quantity and a numeral are more or less than a given quantity. They are not directed to use certain methods. By incorporating the following three process standards, children will be better able to understand the concepts of "more" and "less" and will be better prepared for future lessons involving counting on.

**Representation** Children use counters to represent their understanding of the number relationship of one more or one less than a given number.

**Connections** Children make connections between counting, the mathematical concepts of "more" and "less," and everyday language that indicates more or less.

**Communication** Children explain how they knew how many counters to use to show "more" and "less" than a given number. They talk about their representations using phrases like "the next number" and "the number before."

## Teaching Plan

**Materials** → Student pages 28–29; 10 counters and one sheet of colored construction paper per child; drawing paper; crayons; also, an illustrated counting book

USING TEN PAINTBRUSHES or some other easily distinguishable manipulative, count from 1 to 10 in unison with the children. After each number ask the children how many brushes there are. After you have reached 10, count back to 1, again stopping after each number to ask the class how many brushes are left. This activity gives children a visual representation of one more, then one less.

Choose a counting book and introduce it to the class. Have children discuss the cover and predict what they think the book is about. Read the book through once to the class.

Give each child ten counters and the colored construction paper to use as a mat. Then reread the book, stopping to discuss the numbers represented on each page. Count the number of objects on the page with the children. Ask them how many objects would there be if there was one more or one less object. Have the children use their counters to show the number of objects. Do not mix the concepts of more and less on the same page so that children do not confuse the two concepts.

Have children show their representations and tell how they knew how many counters to place on the mat. Children may explain their thinking in one of the following ways:

- There are 5 [objects] on the page. When I count, I know that 6 comes right after 5, so 6 is one more than 5.
- There are 4 [objects] on the page. Since 3 is the number that comes right before 4, it must be one less than 4.
- First I counted 6 things. Then I added 1 more, and that made 7.

NEXT, GIVE EACH CHILD A SHEET of drawing paper and crayons. Model for them how to fold the paper first vertically and then horizontally. After they have opened the sheet of paper, ask them to trace the fold lines to make 4 sections. Hold up your own paper and point out the top left-hand section. Ask them to draw 6 circles in the section and then write the number of circles. Check to make sure that children have drawn 6 circles and written the numeral 6 in the top left-hand section.

In the lower left section, have children draw the same number of circles they drew above and then draw one more circle. *How many circles are there in this section now?* Have them write the numeral for the number of circles in the section. As you observe children drawing their pictures, ask them how they knew which numeral to write. *What number is one more than 6?*

In the top right section of the paper, have children choose the number of circles between one and ten that they want to draw. Have them write the numeral for the number of circles they drew. Then in the lower right square, have them draw 1 less circle than they just drew in the top right section and have them write the number.

f.y.i.
-------------------------------------
Some suggested titles for counting books are:

*The Very Hungry Caterpillar,* by Eric Carle

*Ten Black Dots,* by Donald Crews

*Fish Eyes: A Book You Can Count On,* by Lois Ehlert

*Feast for 10,* by Cathryn Falwell

*Ten Apples Up On Top,* by Theo Le Sieg

*Anno's Counting Book,* by Anno Mitsumasa

*Ten in Bed,* by Mary Rees

Have children share their drawings and tell how they knew how many circles to draw and what numbers to write.

### Methods Children Might Use to Show the Concept of One More

- They drew lines from the top 6 circles, matched the lines with circles, and then drew 1 more.
- They recounted the top 6 circles, drew that many circles in the section below, and added 1 more.
- They knew that 1 more means the next number, so they drew 7 circles.

### Methods Children Might Use to Show the Concept of One Less

- They put an "X" through one of the circles in the top right section and copied the rest of the circles in the section below. They counted the number of circles they had drawn and wrote the number.
- They covered one circle out of the group they had drawn in the top section and then drew the number of circles that were left in the lower right section.
- They knew that "one less" is the number before the original number so they drew that many circles.

Children often have made stronger connections to the concept of "one more" rather than "one less," possibly because they have had more experience with counting forward than with counting back. Talk with them about what "more" and "less" mean. Then have children compare quantities where they focus on both "more" and "less." An activity that you might do would be to make a group of 5 counters and a group of 6 counters. Ask children to tell which group has more. Then, have them tell which group has less. Do several similar activities with the children. You might want to be aware of other situations in which the concepts of more and less can be reinforced.

## Student Pages

Student page 28 has four illustrated problems. For each problem, children draw one more or one less than the number of objects shown and write the corresponding numerals. Read the directions aloud to the children before they complete each section of the page. On student page 29, children draw circles showing one more and one less than the five circles shown. They also write the corresponding numerals. Read the directions aloud to the children.

## Assessment

During the counting book activity, you had the opportunity to assess how well children understood the concepts of "one more" and "one less" through their use of counters and through their explanations of how they determined how many counters to use. You observed and discussed children's work as they drew circles and then illustrated "one more" and "one less" than their original drawings. During this activity, you could evaluate their comprehension of the lesson objective by listening to how they figured out how to draw one more or one less than the original number of circles. You can also use the student pages to see how well children can apply what they learned in the lesson.

## NCTM Standards Summary

Children connected counting with quantity and with numerals. They then made connections to the concepts of "more" and "less" and to everyday language used for communicating "more" and "less." They counted the number of objects in pictures and represented that number using counters. They showed their understanding of "one more" and "one less" by representing the concepts with counters and by drawing pictures. Children shared their representations of "one more" and "one less" with their classmates and they communicated how they determined how many objects to draw. They also explained the methods they used for deciding what number was one more or one less than the original number.

**Answers**

*Page 28*
Check children's drawings
1. 4
2. 8
3. 5
4. 7
*Page 29*

Check children's drawings
1. 6
2. 4

# Determining One More, One Less

## Draw 1 more. Write the numeral.

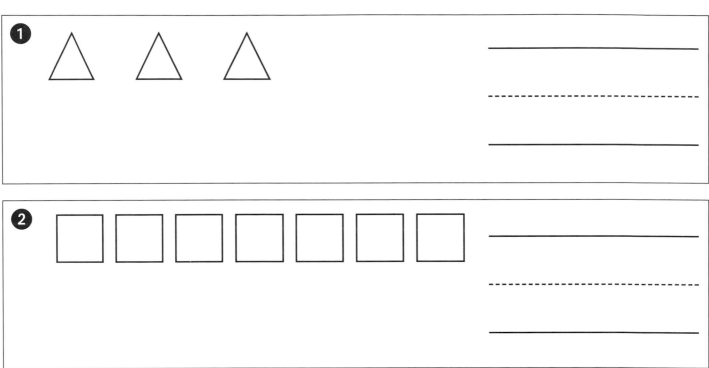

## Show one less. Write the numeral.

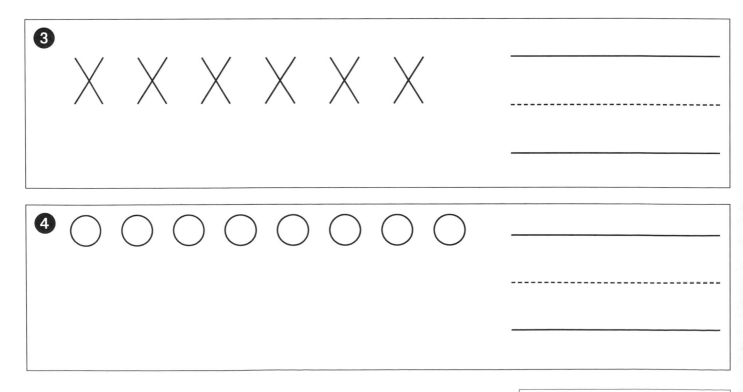

**Standard 1** Number and Operation

# Determining One More, One Less

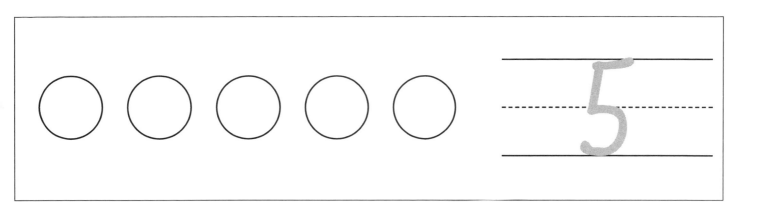

## Draw 1 more. Write the numeral.

**1**

## Draw 1 less. Write the numeral.

# Linking Numerals and Number Words

## Introduction

------------------------------------

**Objective** → Children will match numerals with the written word names for the numbers 1 through 6.

**Context** → Children have learned to count to ten and understand cardinality. They will go on to learn to use visual patterns to determine quantity and to find different ways to represent numbers.

## NCTM Standards Focus

What makes this standards-based lesson worthy of inclusion is the richness of the connections children form among the representations of numerals as numbers, number words, and dots. The key to the lesson is active involvement of the children as they match numerals and number words and, in their own way, represent quantities with dots. They also connect to real life by representing each number with objects found in the classroom. Throughout the lesson, children develop their own strategies and techniques for identifying numerals, number words, and quantities.

**Connections** Children make connections between counting, quantity, and written number words. Using their knowledge of counting, they also connect number words to numerical order.

**Representation** Children represent a quantity in three different ways: as a numeral, as a dot pattern, and as a word.

## Teaching Plan

**Materials** → Student pages 34–35; classroom objects

BEGIN THE LESSON BY DRAWING one dot on the board or the overhead. *How many dots are there?* Have a volunteer write the numeral. *What do the dot and the number show?* Wait until a volunteer has said the word "one." Then write "one" on the board below the numeral and the dot. *What are the letters in "one"?* Write the word again, saying each letter as you write it. Now point to the dot, the numeral, and the word. *How many different ways have we shown the same number?* Give the children the two student pages and ask them to cut out the cards with numerals and number words on them. Have them look for the numeral 1 and represent the number with dots. Ask them to find the number word "one" and match the numeral and number word. Repeat the activity for the numerals 2–6.

Have several children find objects in the classroom that represent each number from one to six. Encourage children to tell how the classroom objects show the numbers in the same way or in a different way as they are shown on the cards. Then have them attach the correct number word card and numeral card to each collection of objects.

Have children think about how they know which number word and numeral go with which group of objects. Then have volunteers explain how they recognized which number word and numeral card matched the number of objects. Children are making important connections between counting, quantity, numerals, and number words.

To remember how each number word looked, children may have used one of the following reading strategies:

- They might look at the first letter of each number word and remember which word began with that letter. For example, "one" is the only word that begins with "o."
- They might sound out each word phonetically by looking at the letters in the word and by figuring out which sounds they made. Then they match these sounds to the sounds they hear when they say the number.
- They might use the shapes of the words to recognize each word. For example, "one" and "six" are the only words that do not have any tall letters.

CONCLUDE THE LESSON BY ASSIGNING six children the numbers 1 through 6. Explain that they are going to place their numbers in numerical order, using the number word cards. Call on the children, in random order, asking them to place their number word cards in order at the front of the class. Ask children to explain how they decided where to place their number word. You could also do this activity with the numeral cards or with dot representations of each number.

The following activities lend themselves to small group or math center activities.

**Activity 1: Making a counting book** Make several copies of the two student pages and cut the cards apart. Mix the numeral cards and place them in a box. Then mix the number word cards and place them in another box. Each child chooses a numeral from the first box and matches it with the appropriate number word from the second box. The child then pastes the two cards on a sheet of paper and illustrates the paper with as many objects as the numeral and number word represent. Collect the pages from the children and make them into a counting book.

**Activity 2: Number concentration** Have children work in pairs, using one set of their numeral cards and number word cards to play "Number Concentration." One partner shuffles the cards together and lays them out in rows, face down. Partners then take turns turning over two cards. If the cards match (6 with "six," for example) they keep the matched pair of cards. If the cards do not match, they turn them back over, face down. The goal is to make as many matches as possible. For a greater challenge, two sets of cards can be used.

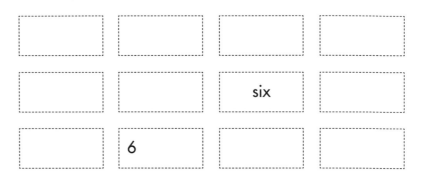

**Activity 3: Number of sides of shapes** Give each child a set of the number words and a group of two-dimensional shapes. Ask them to attach the number words to the shapes with the corresponding number of sides. For example, (triangle) three; (trapezoid, rectangle, square) four; (pentagon) five; (hexagon) six. Ask children which number words they have not used. (one, two) Have them make a simple drawing to illustrate each of these number words (e.g., a single line to illustrate "one").

**Activity 4: Number puzzles** Give each child 6 index cards. Have children make a squiggly cut through each card. They then either paste or write a number word on one piece and draw the corresponding number of dots on the other piece. They do this for each number word, one through six. Children then place all the pieces in a box and mix them up. They use the pieces as a puzzle, matching the words with the number of dots.

 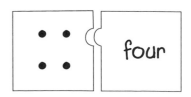

## Student Pages

Student page 34 has the numerals 1 through 6 printed on rectangular cards. After children have cut out the cards, they will draw dots on the cards to show the quantity each numeral expresses. Student page 35 has the number words "one" through "six" printed on rectangular cards. Children will match these number words to the numerals and dots.

## Assessment

During the first activity, you observed the children as they represented numerals with the corresponding number of dots. You had the opportunity to assess whether they used one-to-one counting to determine the correct number of dots or used a pattern to indicate the quantity. As you watched them work and listened to them explain how they matched number words to numerals, you were able to assess the strategies they used for associating numerals with their number words. You were also able to evaluate if children demonstrated an understanding of the connections between numerals, number words, and quantities and then connected this understanding to numerical order.

## NCTM Standards Summary

Children made connections between the numerals 1 through 6, the corresponding number words, and the quantities each represents. They expressed 1 through 6 as numerals and as quantities and then matched them to the written word for each number. Next, they connected these representations to everyday classroom objects. Finally, they placed the number words in numerical order based on their previous knowledge of counting and their newly gained recognition of number words and their connections to the numerals and quantities they represent.

# Linking Numerals and Number Words

## Cut out each number card.

| | |
|---|---|
| 1 | 4 |
| 2 | 5 |
| 3 | 6 |

**Standard 1** Number and Operation

# Linking Numerals and Number Words

**Cut out each number word card.**

| | |
|---|---|
| one | four |
| two | five |
| three | six |

# Developing Number Sense: Groups of Five

## Introduction

**Objective** → Children will recognize, identify, and create groups of 5.

**Context** → Children have experienced a wide range of activities to recognize and identify groups of 1 through 4. Future lessons may include activities to investigate the concept of 0.

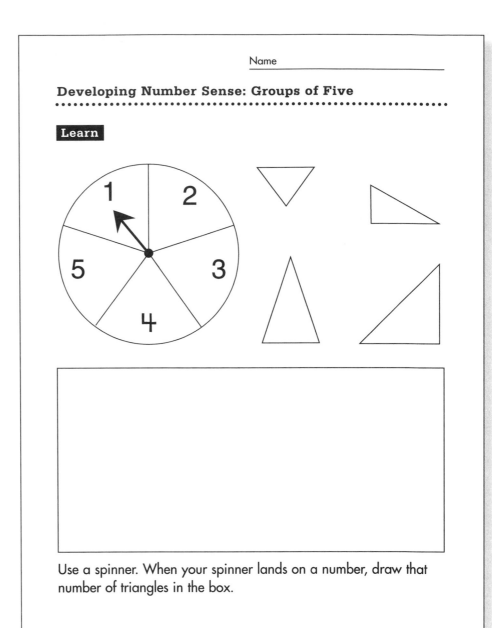

Name _____

**Developing Number Sense: Groups of Five**

Learn

Use a spinner. When your spinner lands on a number, draw that number of triangles in the box.

## NCTM Process Standards Analysis and Focus

The standards analysis examines how the process standards have been incorporated into the above lesson. By increasing the focus on three of the process standards, a more effective and meaningful lesson can be presented. The suggestions offered can help you to think about how this might be accomplished.

**Connections** A suggestion in the teacher notes has children connect the number 5 with fingers and toes.

*Suggestion* → **Provide a broader range of activities to build and extend children's awareness of the number 5. Include drawing, writing, and counting activities to help show how mathematical ideas are connected to everyday experiences.**

Name _____

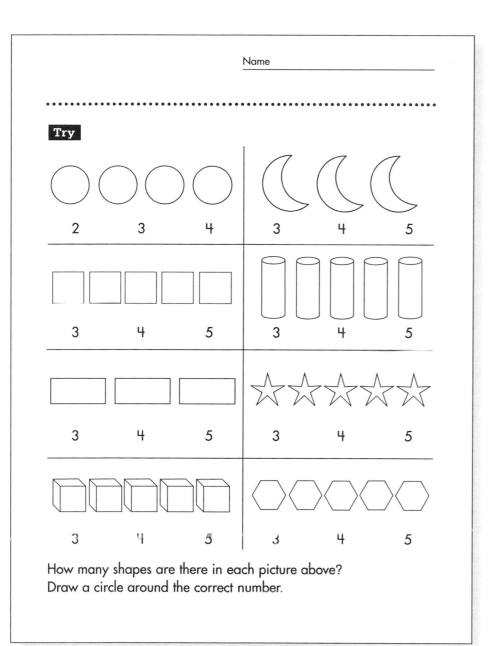

**Try**

How many shapes are there in each picture above?
Draw a circle around the correct number.

**Representation** The lesson offers limited representations of 5. Children play with a spinner and complete worksheet activities that call for counting objects and circling numbers.

*Suggestion →* Provide opportunities to manipulate objects to create groups of 5. Use visual models to help children recognize and identify groups of 5 in a variety of contexts. These activities will help children connect symbolic representation with amount.

**Communication** Opportunities to talk about math appear in a warm-up reading of a poem, simple questions, and directions to children.

*Suggestion →* Provide time for children to discuss and clarify their understandings of 5. Mathematical vocabulary expands as children share ideas, listen to classmates, hear stories read aloud, and create and discuss illustrations to describe the number 5.

**Problem Solving** Because the purpose of the lesson is to recognize and identify, problem solving is not called for.

**Reasoning and Proof** Neither strategies that help children identify quantity nor methods for checking answers are included in the lesson.

The teaching plan that follows shows how the suggestions for increasing the focus on the process standards can be implemented.

## Revised Teaching Plan

**Materials** → Chart paper; markers; counters and other manipulatives; large index cards, 5 per child

## Teaching the Lesson

TO INTRODUCE THE MATH CONCEPT, begin the lesson with a shared reading of "Five Little Monkeys" or another favorite number chant that highlights the number 5. As you share the chant, emphasize the numbers by saying them louder than the other words. Use your hands or count out 5 volunteers to dramatize the actions for a second retelling of the chant.

WRITE A LARGE 5 ON CHART PAPER. Have children say the number aloud as you write it. Then invite volunteers to trace the number with their fingers. Make connections between the number of characters in the rhyme (5) and other things children know that come in groups of 5. *You just heard a poem about 5 (monkeys). What else comes in groups of 5? Is anyone 5 years old? What does that mean?* Children need many opportunities to connect the numeral with the amount it represents. Encouraging communication about familiar objects that are grouped in 5s, such as 5 toes, 5 fingers, 5 buttons on a shirt, or 5 players on a basketball team, helps children think about different representations of 5 that they are familiar with and reinforces the connection between numeral and quantity. Illustrate children's ideas on chart paper. Each time, have children count the objects as you illustrate them; then write the numeral next to the illustration.

ORGANIZE SMALL-GROUP LEARNING ACTIVITIES to further develop children's understandings of the concept of 5. Select from activities below to explore the concept in a variety of contexts. Rotate the activities throughout your day or week according to your schedule. These activities help children connect concrete and oral representations for the number 5. The more experiences children have with this, the more automatic number recognition will become.

**Activity 1** Place 5 counters on a table. *Who can tell me about the number of counters? How did you figure out how many there are?* Allow time for children to discuss their strategies. Count aloud as a volunteer points to each counter. Say the total number aloud. Repeat with another set of counters. Vary the arrangement to reinforce the idea that the quantity does not change. For example, place the counters in a row or in a circle. Also vary the number of counters, using 3 or 4 sometimes, to be sure children are looking at the *number* of counters each time. *Were some arrangements easier to identify? Why?*

**Activity 2** Place construction paper, inkpads, and markers on a table. Demonstrate how to press your thumb on the inkpad and make 5 thumbprints. Show examples of ways to add lines to each print to make 5 thumbprint critters. Have children write or dictate captions to describe their pictures. For example, "5 tigers are sitting by a lake." Have other children count the thumbprint drawings to check the number.

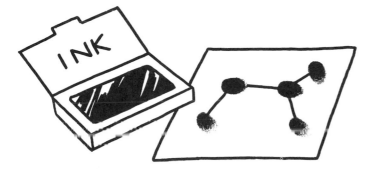

**Activity 3** Fill 10–12 plastic jars with a predetermined assortment of objects such as teddy-bear counters, marbles, erasers, and pennies. Vary the number placed in each jar from 1 to 5. Make number cards to correspond with the quantities. Have children work together to identify amounts and match the number cards to the correct jar. *Which jars contain 5 items? Tell about the number of items in the other jars. How did you keep track of the items in the jars you counted?* Consider a sorting activity to extend children's thinking. For example, jars with 5 objects and jars with other than 5 objects. Allow time for children to explain how they sorted the jars.

**Activity 4** In advance, prepare index cards by drawing a dotted line down the middle of each card to create two sides. Distribute 5 cards to each child and have children use these cards to create puzzles. Show children how to draw the numeral 5 on the left side of the dotted line and a set of 5 objects to match the numeral on the right side. If possible, create a model for children to use as they create their own puzzles for numbers 1 to 5. When children finish drawing, have them cut on the dotted lines to create two puzzle pieces. Then allow time for children to exchange puzzles with classmates. Have children mix up the pieces and put them back together. Remind children to check the puzzles by saying the number and counting out the objects. Place puzzles in reclosable plastic bags for future independent activities.

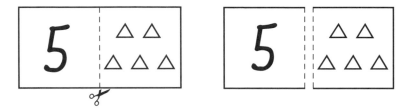

**Activity 5** Create a big book for the number 5. Use large sheets of construction paper for the book pages. Encourage children to find and illustrate classroom objects that can be grouped in sets of 5. Have them draw 5 objects and write the numeral 5 on each page. Encourage children to check their illustrations by counting the objects. Work with children to label the sets of 5, such as 5 chairs, 5 lunchboxes, or 5 plants. Assemble the pages to create a class book. Draw attention to the visual representation and the numeral to help children make connections.

---

### What Might Happen . . . What to Do

Children write the numeral 5 backwards. Use a variety of materials to help children practice forming their numerals. Place tubs of sand in a center for children to use to form and shape their numerals. Create tactile cards for children to trace and feel the shapes of the numerals with their fingers. Use glue to write numerals and sprinkle with sand or seeds to add texture. Draw children's attention to the lines and shapes as they form each one.

---

**Activity 6** Use calculators to reinforce and challenge children's number sense. Have children work in pairs. Distribute a set of number cards for the numbers 1–5. Have one partner select a card and say the number aloud without showing it to the partner. Have the partner find and display the number on the calculator. Allow time for children to share their responses and then switch roles. Calculators provide another form of representation to the number 5.

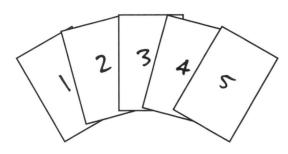

## Student Pages

Children are ready to complete practice exercises similar to those shown on the reduced student pages. When children are finished, have them write or dictate a sentence to go with each picture.

## Assessment

A range of learning activities allowed opportunities for assessing children's understandings of 5. Observing and listening to children describe their illustrations of 5 offered insight about what they know. Constructing puzzles and matching activities with jars provided a context to see if children were able to match symbolic and visual representations of 5 with concrete models.

## NCTM Standards Summary

Making connections and seeing multiple representations of 5 were incorporated into the lesson. Varied learning experiences enabled children to make connections between familiar everyday objects and numerical concepts. In addition, connections were made as children linked mathematical symbols with counting activities. Auditory, visual, and concrete representations of the number 5 allowed children to see how a quantity remains constant regardless of its representation. Repeated opportunities to connect the numeral's representation verbally and in written form reinforced number recognition. Time allotted to discuss strategies and methods for organizing and counting was greatly increased throughout the lesson. These discussions provided a meaningful context in which children were able to use mathematical language as they identified, recognized, and described quantities of 5.

**f.y.i.**

- - - - - - - - - - - - - - - - - - - - - - - - -

As an ongoing activity, read aloud picture books that contain embedded mathematical number themes such as *The Five Chinese Brothers* or *Counting Wildflowers*. Simple story lines with vivid illustrations or photographs offer another context to help children extend their mathematical understandings.

# Standard 2 **Algebra**

**A**T THE KINDERGARTEN LEVEL, algebra includes work with recognizing patterns, function relationships, balance (equality), and comparing the number of objects in two groups. Our lessons are derived from these important topics, and include a lesson on recognizing patterns, a lesson on investigating function relationships, a lesson that investigates balance, and a lesson in which the number of objects in two groups is compared.

Three lessons model how the process standards can be used to teach content. A fourth lesson is a hypothetical textbook lesson that we have revised to be more standards based. These four lessons do not represent the entire curriculum, but rather provide glimpses of how, with a more concentrated effort to incorporate the process standards, better mathematics teaching and learning can be achieved.

In one lesson we have chosen, children recognize and extend patterns. By focusing on the process standards of connections, communication, and representation, children not only draw pictures of their understanding, but also use manipulatives, physical movements, and language. Children are also asked to show different representations of a given pattern.

Another lesson we have chosen helps children to identify and analyze functional relationships. In this lesson, children use reasoning and proof and communication to figure out the inputs or outputs from a "function machine." Children are involved in the problem solving process as they verbalize their thinking as it relates to applying the function relationship.

A third lesson that we have chosen investigates balance. Through the process standards of reasoning and proof and communication, children develop the necessary vocabulary to convey comparisons between the weights of two objects. Children try to predict the relationship between two objects, then use a pan balance to test their conjectures.

The hypothetical textbook lesson that we have chosen to revise has children compare the number of objects in two groups and decide which group has more and which group has fewer. Through better incorporation of the process standards of representation, reasoning and proof, and communication, children will develop and learn new ways to help them recognize which group contains more objects or fewer objects.

## Standard 2 Lessons

------------------------------------

**Investigating Function Relationships**

------------------------------------

**Recognizing Patterns**

------------------------------------

**Investigating Balance**

------------------------------------

**Number Sense: Comparing Groups**

# Recognizing Patterns

## Introduction

------------------------------------

**Objective** → Children will identify, analyze, and extend patterns, and will recognize the same pattern using different materials.

**Context** → Children have counted and written numbers and understand that numbers "face" in different directions such as is the case with the numbers 3 and 5. In subsequent lessons, they will use geometric shapes in patterns and pay attention to the direction the different shapes face.

## NCTM Standards Focus

In this standards-based lesson, children are introduced to what makes a pattern, how to continue a pattern, and how patterns are different and similar. The emphasis throughout the lesson is on children connecting their prior knowledge of details in numbers to details in patterns. They are encouraged to share their thinking and to listen to one another's interpretation of what they are seeing. Since children are encouraged to communicate their understanding, misunderstandings can be dealt with immediately rather than relying mainly on children's pictorial representations, which can be unreliable. At this age, children's verbal ability far exceeds their ability to recreate their understanding with pictures.

**Connections** Children make connections between patterns they make in movement activities and the patterns they make with classroom objects. They analyze and conjecture about similarities and differences between the movement patterns they observe and the patterns they make with classroom objects.

**Communication** Children are asked to explain how they know what comes next in the movement-activity patterns. They describe what they observe in these patterns by concentrating on the three repetitions. They use the same reasoning about patterns when they work with connecting cubes and when they draw what comes next on the student pages.

**Representation** Children use two colors to show patterns with connecting cubes similar to ones that they experienced with movement-activity patterns. They connect the different types of patterns they observed and created with the pictures of patterns on the student pages.

## Teaching Plan

**Materials** → Student pages 48–49; for each child: a small plastic bag with 10 connecting cubes in two colors; crayons

Gather children in a large open area in the classroom. Have 7 children stand in front of the group. Whisper specific instructions to each child so that the rest of the class cannot hear what you are saying. Have the first child remain standing with arms to the side. Ask the second child to sit down and cross his or her legs "pretzel-style" with hands placed in the lap. Repeat these directions individually to each of the 5 remaining children so that the last child, the seventh, remains standing with arms at his or her side.

*Who thinks he or she knows what the next child will do?* Have a volunteer come forward and show what he or she thinks the next child should do. Ask the rest of the class if they agree or disagree with what the volunteer thinks should come next in the lineup. Then, have one child explain how he or she knew what the eighth child should do.

---

### What Might Happen . . . What to Do

Some children might want to do something entirely different with the pattern. It is important to ask how the child knew that kneeling, instead of standing, would be next in the lineup based on what came before. Call attention to the existing pattern, focusing on extending that pattern, not beginning a different one. Often, other children will disagree with a child who tries something new and can help this child understand that what comes next has to be something that has already been seen.

---

Have children in the lineup sit down, and call on 7 different children to come forward. The second pattern can be a "hands on the head, hands on the waist" pattern. The third pattern can be "child facing forward, child facing backwards."

Each time you create a new pattern with a group of children, ask questions to determine how children know what comes next in the pattern. Encourage children to describe the pattern. If the word *pattern* has not been used before, write and illustrate the word. Have children tell what they think it means.

NEXT, HAVE ALL CHILDREN return to their seats as you distribute the plastic bags. Invite children to make a pattern with 6 cubes, alternating the colors. Have children raise their hands when they've connected the 6 cubes.

**f.y.i.**

---

If you have a Math Word Wall, write the word "pattern" there. If you do not have a Math Word Wall, you might want to start one by taping a sheet of chart paper to a wall in a place that can easily be seen by all. Write the math words on the chart paper. Include an illustration and a simple definition.

Have volunteers describe what they have done and what would come next. Since children will have different color combinations in their bags, encourage several children to share their responses and their thinking.

Then, have children complete their patterns using all 10 cubes. *If you had one more cube, what do you think would come next? How do you know?* Call on a few children to articulate their explanations.

Ask children to put all the cubes back in their bags and then exchange bags with a partner. Repeat the activity described above, making sure that children stop after making a pattern with 6 cubes. At this point, have partners exchange information by explaining to one another what would come next and how they know. Then, invite partners to extend one another's patterns with the remaining cubes.

After putting away the cubes, refer back to the movement activities done earlier in the lesson. *How are the movement-activity patterns we did earlier different from the connecting-cube patterns?* Children should be able to talk about how the pattern components were different, that is, children versus connecting cubes. Also, when children made up patterns, they paid attention to the movements of their classmates, while with the cubes they paid attention to the colors. *How are the movement patterns similar to the connecting-cube patterns?*

CONCLUDE THE LESSON by distributing copies of student page 48. Instruct children to make the same kind of pattern they just made with the connecting cubes. You might want to send the second student page home to be completed or place it in the math center. On both pages, children have additional opportunities to reinforce their knowledge of patterns.

## Student Pages

Page 48 has three rows of cubes with directions to show a pattern and what comes next. On page 49, children color two patterns and show what comes next.

## Assessment

There were many opportunities to check how children paid attention to details that make up patterns. Children's understanding could be assessed regarding how patterns could be made from movements and how similar patterns could be made using connecting cubes or pictures. Observing children's actions and listening to their descriptions about what makes a pattern a pattern and whether or not they agreed or disagreed with a classmate's interpretation of what came next in a pattern provided information about their level of understanding.

## NCTM Standards Summary

Children communicated their understanding of what they were observing as a pattern. They connected this knowledge to recreate patterns. They represented these patterns using connecting cubes. They extended the connections they first made with concrete materials to represent the patterns with pictures. They communicated their understanding by responding to questions about what they thought would come next in a given pattern and about how they knew. They analyzed differences and similarities between movement-activity patterns, connecting-cube patterns, and pictorial patterns.

**Answers**

*Page 48*
1–3. Children alternate colors beginning and ending with the same color.

*Page 49*
1–2. Children alternate colors beginning and ending with the same color.
3. Answers may vary.

# Recognizing Patterns

## Use 2 colors to show a pattern. Then show what comes next.

**1**

**2**

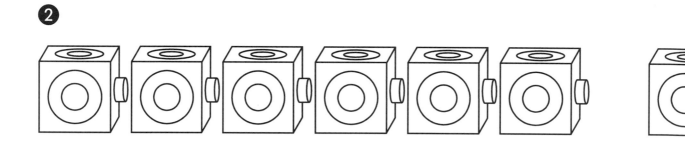

**3**

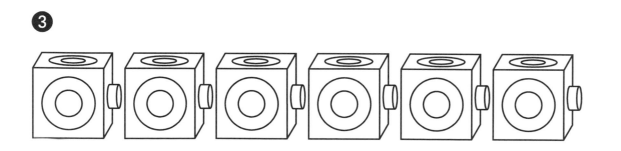 

**Standard 2** Algebra

Name

# Recognizing Patterns

**Use 2 colors to show a pattern. Then show what comes next.**

**1**

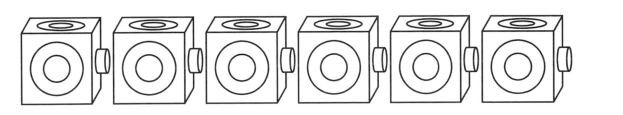 

**2**

**Make up your own pattern using 2 different shapes.
Then show what comes next.**

**3**

# Investigating Function Relationships

## Introduction

-----------------------------------

**Objective** → Children will identify, analyze, and solve functions with verbal rules and pictures.

**Context** → Children have learned to count using one-to-one correspondence. They are familiar with simple patterns and different geometric shapes. In future lessons, they will use their knowledge of functions and function machines as they do formal addition and subtraction.

## NCTM Standards Focus

During this standards-based lesson, children use observation, recorded information, and shared verbal explanations to build an understanding of what functions are and how they can be used. Sometimes children are given function rules with illustrations or even verbally, giving them little opportunity for critical thinking and for making connections. When children are encouraged to explore and make their own connections, they develop understanding that they can draw upon later.

**Reasoning and Proof** Children make and investigate predictions. When they share answers, they have to explain how they know. They explain their reasoning and justify their answers by referring to previously done examples.

**Communication** As they investigate patterns, look for function rules, and explain their thinking, children have many opportunities to express mathematical ideas coherently and clearly to their classmates as well as to the teacher.

**Problem Solving** First, children apply strategies to solve problems, then they adapt the strategies to new situations.

## Teaching Plan

**Materials** → Student pages 54–55; pattern blocks; large box; chart paper; small and large attribute blocks

IN ADVANCE, prepare a large box to be used as a "function machine." Cut out three large holes, as follows: one in the back for the teacher to put her or his hand into; one on the left side for the shapes to be put into; and one on the right side for the shapes to come out of. You might also want to place a small container with extra shapes inside the box in order to easily access additional blocks as you need them.

If you don't have the time or the materials to construct the "function box," you might draw a box on the board and ask children to imagine that you are putting the blocks into it. Or you might just use a box that you put some blocks into and then take some out of according to the rule you are using.

Gather children in a large open area in the classroom. Introduce the large box as a special box that makes things happen to the pattern blocks that are put into it. *When I put things into this box, something will happen. It is your job to figure out the rule for what happens. Then you can predict what will come out.*

Each time you put pattern blocks into the box or take some out, be sure to tell children how many are going in or coming out. Tell the name of the shape as well. Do the activity fairly slowly to allow all children to follow along and take in the information without becoming confused.

PICK UP 1 ORANGE SQUARE pattern block and place it in the box with your right hand. With your left hand, remove 2 orange squares from the box. *I put 1 orange square into the box. I took 2 orange squares out. What happened?* Have volunteers tell what they think happened. Suggestions might include, "You took out 1 more than you put in," "You added 1 more to the right side," or "The number doubled." Encourage children to think of more than one way to describe what happened.

Draw a large box on a sheet of chart paper, and label the left side IN and the right side OUT. Record the number of pattern blocks you put into the box. Then record the number of blocks you removed. You may also want to draw the shapes on the chart paper next to the numbers so children can see everything you're doing.

Follow the same procedure with other pattern blocks. Place 1 yellow hexagon into the box and remove 2 yellow hexagons. *What do you think the rule is this time?* Children should see that the function machine again doubles the number of blocks that are initially placed in the box. Next, put 1 tan rhombus into the box. Finally, put 1 red trapezoid into the box. Each time put 1 block into the box and take out 2 of the same shape. Record the numbers and shapes on the chart paper.

NEXT, PLACE 1 GREEN TRIANGLE in the box and ask children to think about what will come out. *If the rule is the same as it was for the square, the hexagon, the rhombus, and the trapezoid, what do you think should come out of the box when I put in 1 green triangle?* Have children share their answers and explain how they knew that 2 triangles would emerge. Children should be able to explain the rule: if 1 goes in, 2 come out.

### What Might Happen . . . What to Do

Some children might come up with rules that are not related to the activity and are not able to answer the questions because they do not understand what they are being asked to do. In this instance refer back to the first block you put in the box and ask very specific questions about what is happening. *What shape went into the box?*

*How many went in? When the shapes came out, were they still the same shapes? How many shapes came out? Does this happen every time?* Go through each shape in a similar way. In the beginning this will help children to think through what they need to do to solve the problem.

Continue the lesson by placing 1 red trapezoid in the box and having 3 red trapezoids come out. Then put 1 tan rhombus into the box and have 3 tan rhombuses come out. Finally, put in 1 yellow hexagon and have 3 yellow hexagons come out. Each time ask children to tell what they think the rule is. Then put 1 orange square into the box and have children predict what should come out. Encourage children to explain how they know.

Conclude the lesson by using the same-color attribute blocks. Put 1 large triangle into the box and have 1 small triangle come out. Repeat the activity three more times, each time putting a large shape into the box and having a small version of the same shape come out. Finally, show children a small rectangle. *This rectangle came out of the box. What do you think went into the box?* Children should be able to explain the rule: a large shape goes in and a small shape comes out.

Distribute student page 54. As children work individually on the problems, ask specific questions. *What do you think comes out if _____ goes in?* Encourage children to explain their reasoning. Have children prove their answers by referring back to previously completed examples.

## Extension

Introduce the doubling rule to children as follows:

- Place 1 square in the box and have 2 squares come out.
- Place 2 squares in the box and have 4 squares come out.
- Place 3 squares in the box and have 6 squares come out.

Do all the ins and outs and record each one before asking children how many they think will come out when you place 4 squares in the box. Have children consult one another before they reply. Have children tell the rule. Then have them explain how they figured it out.

## Student Pages

Student page 54 has more activities of the kind that were done with the whole class. Student page 55 can be assigned to be done later or as homework. The problems are similar to those on student page 54 and reinforce children's understanding of simple functions.

## Assessment

As children responded to questions asked during the class activities, it was possible to assess both their understanding of what a function is and how to determine what will be "going in" or "coming out." Every time children explained their answers and generalized a rule, there was an opportunity to further check children's understanding. In addition, the homework assignment reinforced whether children were able to solve simple function problems.

## NCTM Standards Summary

Children made many connections between counting and recognizing "how many" are in small sets. They recognized shapes as being the same or similar. During the whole class activities, children predicted outcomes and explained their reasoning for their answers. They communicated their thinking when they generated rules for the different activities, shared how they drew their conclusions, and stated the strategies they used in the problem-solving situation.

**Answers**

*Page 54*
1. 2 squares
2. 1 triangle

*Page 55*
1. 1 small rectangle
2. 1 small triangle
3. 1 large circle

# Investigating Function Relationships

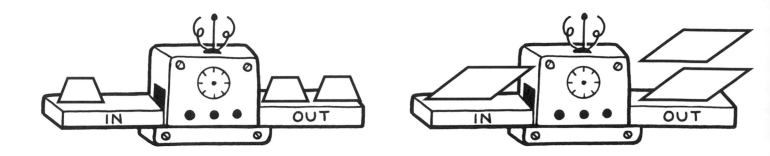

**Draw what comes out.**

**1**

**Draw what goes in.**

**2**

**Standard 2** Algebra

# Investigating Function Relationships

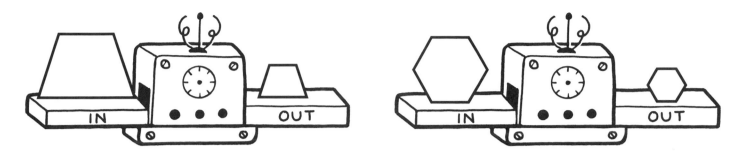

**Draw what comes out.**

**1**

**2**

**Draw what goes in.**

**3**

# Investigating Balance

## Introduction

- - - - - - - - - - - - - - - - - - - - - - - -

**Objective** → Children will determine whether objects are heavier or lighter than another object by feel and with a balance scale.

**Context** → Children have compared groups of objects and described differences in size and number. This is the first lesson they have had on heavier and lighter using a balance scale.

## NCTM Standards Focus

Children use their tactile observations of the size and shape of objects to determine what they think will happen when the objects are placed on a pan balance. They predict what will happen with objects that they can see but not pick up.

**Reasoning and Proof** Children draw on their everyday experiences to predict what will happen when everyday objects are placed on a pan balance. They test their conjectures by placing objects on the balance. Children work at an abstract level when they have to reason about the relationships between objects that are represented on a balance.

**Communication** Children develop the vocabulary of comparison and use it in their work with the balance. They share their understandings first by the conjectures they make and then by analyzing what happens as they place objects on the pan balance.

## Teaching Plan

**Materials** → Student pages 60–61; chart paper; simple pan balance; a variety of classroom objects for use on the balance

**Preparation** → Before beginning the lesson, divide a sheet of chart paper (or use the board) into three columns—one with a pan balance showing the left side lower than the right side; one with a pan balance showing the right side lower than the left side; one with a pan balance showing both sides level.

SHOW CHILDREN A PAN BALANCE and have them tell what they know about it and how they have used it. Then show them two different-sized similar objects, such as a large teddy bear and a small teddy bear. Have children hold the two objects and discuss their attributes, such as size, color, softness, and weight. Then ask children to predict what would happen if one object were put on either side of the pan balance. As children respond, keep asking what information they used to make their prediction. Encourage children to draw on their personal experiences, such as being on a seesaw, as they justify their answers. Record children's responses on the chart paper with tally marks below the appropriate pictures.

**f.y.i.**

--------------------------------------

Often children equate heaviest with biggest. Make sure that some of the larger objects you choose are lighter than corresponding smaller objects.

---

### What Might Happen . . . What to Do

--------------------------------------------------------------------

Some children might find it difficult to predict how the balance will respond to objects placed on it, or they might not be able to recognize which object is heavier. Give these children ample opportunities to use the balance to compare different objects before you ask them to make predictions. Ask them to tell which object makes one side go down. If children are insecure about making predictions about which of two objects is heavier or lighter, give them objects to compare that are markedly different.

---

HAVE TWO CHILDREN place the teddy bears on the balance. Have them tell why they think one side went down or why the balance stayed level. Have children explain their reasoning and compare these responses to their predictions.

Remove the bears from the balance and choose two other objects, such as wooden blocks, for children to observe. Have children handle the objects after you choose them and before they make their predictions. Ask children what will help them make a good prediction. Some children may say that if they hold one item in one hand and one in another it is easier to compare them. Have children talk about how they determine which object is heavier and let children try each other's ideas.

Take this opportunity to introduce the proper vocabulary and have children tell what each word means. Record words as they occur on chart paper. Some words that might come up in the discussion are: *heavy, light, heavier, lighter, balance, weights, up, down, level.*

**f.y.i.**

--------------------------------------

If you have a Math Word Wall, write the words there. If you do not have a Math Word Wall, you might want to start one by taping a sheet of chart paper to a wall in a place that can easily be seen by all. Write the math words on the chart paper. Include a simple illustration and definition.

As mentioned earlier, make sure children have the opportunity to see a smaller object that is heavier. Give children the opportunity to handle the objects before placing them on the balance. After the objects have been placed on the balance, discuss children's predictions and how they aligned with what happened. Make sure children discuss the fact that the larger item might not be the heavier and that they may need more than visual clues to help them predict which object is heavier. Help children understand that the important attributes are not always the visible ones.

Tell children that you want them to place objects on the balance so that the right side goes down. Choose an object and let children handle it. Then place a block on the left side of the balance. Challenge children to choose another object and place it on the balance so that the right side goes down. For example, the object you choose might be a small block. Then children might choose a book to place in the pan on the right. Repeat the activity a number of times, sometimes putting the object you choose in the pan on the left and sometimes putting it in the pan on the right. This will give children opportunities to find objects that are lighter or heavier than the one you choose. As they do the activity, model using the appropriate vocabulary and encourage children to use the terms introduced earlier in the lesson.

## Student Pages

Student page 60 asks children to ring the object that is heavier. Student page 61 asks children to ring the object that is lighter. You might want to send these pages home so that children can familiarize family members with the math concepts they are learning at school. You might also place one or both pages in the math center to provide children with additional practice.

## Assessment

During this lesson, there were several opportunities to assess children's understanding of the balance scale and how it responds to objects placed on it. By the end of the lesson, you were able to assess which children understood that heavier things make a balance go down. In addition, you were able to observe how children reasoned as they made predictions. Children's thinking became apparent as they explained how they drew their conclusions.

## NCTM Standards Summary

Children used their tactile observations of size and shape of objects and connected these experiences to what happened when objects were placed on the pan balance. They used reasoning as they predicted what would happen to the balance once objects were placed on it. Through their observations and communication, they shared their understanding of what happened. They connected the hands-on activities with the balance to the abstract ones on the student pages.

**Answers**

*Page 60*
1. large potato
2. large basketball
3. watermelon
4. flowerpot

*Page 61*
1. box of cereal
2. chair
3. fork
4. pencil

# Investigating Balance

## Ring the object that is heavier.

# Investigating Balance

**Ring the object that is lighter.**

# Comparing Groups

## Introduction

**Objective** → Children will compare 2 groups to determine which has more and which has fewer.

**Context** → Children have completed lessons in which they have identified numbers 1–6. In future lessons, children will continue to work on identifying numbers up to 12.

---

Name _____

### Comparing Groups

**Learn**

Which box has more squares? Ring the box.

**Try**

Which box has more triangles? Ring the box.

**Practice**

Which box has more circles? Ring the box.

---

## NCTM Process Standards Analysis and Focus

The standards analysis examines how the process standards have been incorporated into the above lesson. By increasing the focus on three of the process standards, a more effective and meaningful lesson can be presented. The suggestions offered can help you to think about how this might be accomplished.

**Representation** Activity pages present pictures of objects for children to compare. A suggestion in the teacher notes encourages teachers to use dot cards to play a card game.

*Suggestion* → **Use of concrete and pictorial representations of numbers will help build strategies to identify amounts and make comparisons. Locating numbers on a number line will provide another model for comparing numbers.**

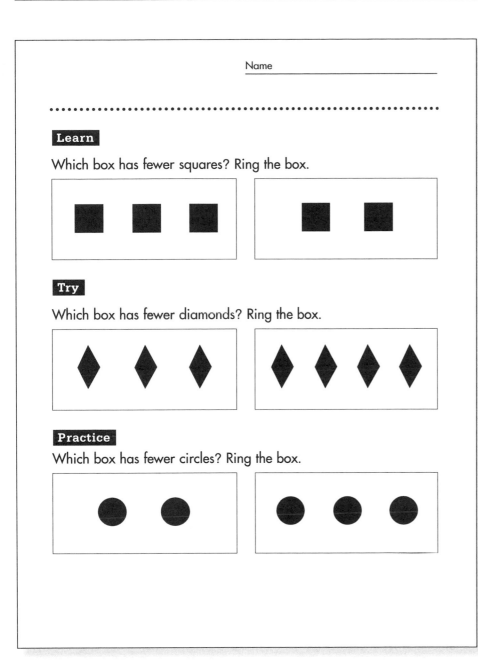

Name _____

**Learn**

Which box has fewer squares? Ring the box.

**Try**

Which box has fewer diamonds? Ring the box.

**Practice**

Which box has fewer circles? Ring the box.

**Reasoning and Proof** Children are asked to compare amounts; however, there is no discussion of how they know which set has more or fewer as the sets are compared.

*Suggestion →* **Have children explain the strategies they use to identify and compare amounts. As they determine which set has more or fewer objects and explain how they know, children's understanding will be reinforced.**

**Communication** Communication opportunities are limited to answering literal questions. Suggestions in the teacher notes include activities in which children describe different amounts of snack items and discuss which amount they would prefer.

*Suggestion →* **Communication and Reasoning and Proof should be heavily integrated throughout the lesson. By discussing similarities and differences between groups and explaining how they know which amount is greater and which is less, children will become better problem-solvers.**

**Problem Solving** Problem solving is not part of this lesson.

**Connections** No connections to prior learning and/or other content areas are incorporated into the lesson.

The teaching plan that follows details how the suggestions made here for incorporating process standards can be implemented.

## Revised Teaching Plan

**Materials** → Objects to count such as buttons, pencils, teddy bear counters; number line; dot cards; number cards; word cards

BEGIN THE LESSON WITH A WARM-UP ACTIVITY to help children compare familiar objects in the classroom. *I wonder if we have more doors than windows. How can we check?* Give children time to look around the room. Work with them to count the doors and windows in order to make a comparison. Conclude by saying that there are more ___ than ___. Invite children to suggest other objects to compare, such as chairs and desks. Have children predict, then verify their predictions by counting. The level of engagement increases when objects familiar to children are incorporated into the activity: children can more readily make connections and build on their knowledge base.

ORGANIZE SMALL-GROUP ACTIVITIES to further develop children's number sense and build strategies for making comparisons. Select from the activities below to explore the concept in a variety of contexts. Rotate the activities throughout your day or week according to your schedule.

**Activity 1** Place two groups of the same kind of object on a table, for example, 4 short pencils and 3 long ones. Ask children to identify the group that has more pencils. Draw children's attention to the difference between the number of objects and their size. As children share ideas, encourage them to use terms such as *more, less, equal, same, fewer,* and *greater*. Repeat the activity with two new groups of objects, making sure to use objects that differ in size, such as standard and jumbo paper clips or big and little buttons. Also try varying the activity by using groups of objects that differ in size yet are equal in number.

## What Might Happen . . . What to Do

Children may confuse size with number of objects. Help children see that it is how many objects, not size, that determines a greater number. Organize two groups of different objects, placing less than 6 in each group. Use short pieces of yarn to illustrate a one-to-one correspondence. Allow time for children to look at the objects to determine which group has the greater number.

**Activity 2** Form two sets using different numbers of teddy bears or other counters. Ask volunteers to count and compare the number of objects in each set. This activity reinforces children's understanding of which number comes first in counting order as well as the concept that the higher they count, the greater the quantity represented. Then, show each number's location on a number line. *What do you notice about the two numbers on the number line? How does the number line show which number is greater? Less?* Repeat the activity several times with different numbers. A number line offers an excellent visual representation for comparing numbers.

**Activity 3** Fill small containers with two colors of connecting cubes for children to count and compare. Create a set of word cards for each container. Use the words *more*, *less*, and *same*. Have children take a container and determine which color there is more of/less of. Show children how to take cubes from a container and connect the cubes to create trains, then place the trains side by side to make a comparison. Have children use word cards to label the trains with the appropriate term. Challenge children to describe their trains using words such as *greater than*, *less than*, *more*, *fewer*, *equal*, and *same*. This activity encourages children to make the connection between a concrete model and the word(s) that describes it.

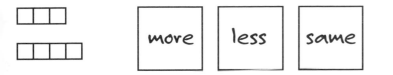

**Activity 4** Use large dot cards to develop the concept of *more* and *less*. Prior to the activity, create a set of dot cards for numbers 1–6 showing different arrangements of dots for each number. For example, you might show the number 2 as illustrated. A second set of dot cards might show the number of dots and include a numeral.

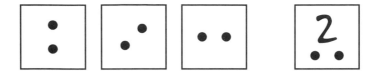

Display a card with a single dot. *How many dots do you see?* Place a card with 2 dots next to the first card. Have children identify the amount and then compare the two cards. *What do you notice about the two cards? What's the same? What's different? How do you know?*

Show another dot card with a different configuration of 2 dots and ask children to identify the quantity. Add a dot card with an arrangement for the number 3. Allow time for children to compare the two cards to determine which card has more or fewer dots. Continue the activity with numbers up to 6. Seeing different configurations for similar quantities helps children develop a repertoire of visual representations. Children will also begin to develop concrete strategies for "reading" amounts.

**Activity 5** Give each child two small paper plates. Provide different colors of play dough for children to use to make creative snacks, then have them use their play-dough snacks to illustrate a comparison. Work with children to write or dictate a sentence that describes their comparison. Encourage children to use words such as *fewer, more, less, equal,* and *same* as they describe the difference in quantities. Allow time for children to share their plates and tell how they knew which plate had more or fewer objects.

**Activity 6** Place different quantities of attribute blocks in individual bags. Organize children into small groups. Have each group organize their blocks to make comparisons. Allow time for each group to compare their quantity of blocks with another group's. Remind children to think about the quantity of blocks rather than attributes. Distribute construction paper to each group and have them illustrate their comparisons. Dictate or write their observations, for example, "The penguin group has more blocks than the rocket group. The penguin group has fewer blocks than the star group."

CONCLUDE THE LESSON BY PLAYING "That's My Number." Give children a clue about a number from 0 to 6. For example, you might say, *My number is less than 4.* Allow time for children to identify all the possible numbers. Reinforce their responses by locating 4 on the number line and naming all the numbers that are less than 4. Consider clues to narrow in on a specific number such as *I'm less than 4 and I'm greater than 1.* As an alternative strategy, consider saying, *I'm less than 4. Can I be 6? Can I be 2? How do you know?*

## Student Pages

Children should now be ready to complete exercises similar to those on the reduced student pages.

## Assessment

When children organized their counters, there were opportunities to probe children's understandings about comparing two sets. Observing children's actions and listening to their responses provided information about their level of understanding. Children's ability to determine which set had more or fewer objects could easily be assessed as children worked with dot cards, created snack plates, and illustrated comparisons with attribute blocks.

## NCTM Standards Summary

Using a broad range of models allowed children to investigate comparisons in a variety of contexts and helped strengthen their understandings. Both similar and different objects were compared to draw children's attention to the number of objects rather than their attributes, specifically size. Throughout the lesson, children were encouraged to explain and justify their thinking. They were encouraged to use information in a logical manner as they explored the concepts of *more* and *less*. Language-rich activities provided a context in which children could discuss and explore ideas with classmates.

# Standard 3 **Geometry**

AT THE KINDERGARTEN LEVEL, geometry includes work with two- and three-dimensional shapes and with describing positions in space. Our lessons are derived from these important topics, and include a lesson on describing positions in space, a lesson on recognizing three-dimensional shapes, a lesson that relates two- and three-dimensional shapes, and a lesson on circles and squares.

Three lessons model how the process standards can be used to teach content. A fourth lesson is a hypothetical textbook lesson that we have revised to be more standards based. These four lessons do not represent the entire curriculum, but rather provide glimpses of how, with a more concentrated effort to incorporate the process standards, better mathematics teaching and learning can be achieved.

In one lesson we have chosen, children describe positions in space. The process standards of connections and communication motivate this lesson as children recall their prior knowledge and experiences to act out words that indicate position. Further connections are made as children connect these movements to other representations.

Another lesson we have chosen is one in which children recognize and identify three-dimensional shapes. By basing this lesson on the process standards of connections, communication, and reasoning and proof, children come up with their own definitions of four shapes by observing their attributes. Children are also given nonexamples of different shapes and asked why the shape is not one of the four.

A third lesson that we have chosen has children match the faces of three-dimensional shapes to the two-dimensional shapes. The process standards of reasoning and proof, connections, and communication are important here, as children physically handle the three-dimensional shapes and list the attributes of each. This helps children to create visual pictures of the faces.

The hypothetical textbook lesson we have chosen to revise is a lesson that has children exploring circles and squares. Through better incorporation of the process standards of reasoning and proof, representation, and communication, children discuss the attributes of each shape. They are to identify those shapes from a group of shapes, and to find examples of these shapes in their everyday environments.

## Standard 3 Lessons

Describing Positions in Space

Recognizing Three-Dimensional Shapes

Relating Two- and Three-Dimensional Shapes

Investigating Circles and Squares

## Describing Positions in Space

### Introduction

**Objective** → Children will describe, name, interpret, and apply ideas of relative position in space.

**Context** → Children have used and described positions of objects when they have sorted classroom items according to attributes. They will continue using descriptive language in future lessons to show position and identify objects.

### NCTM Standards Focus

In this standards-based lesson, children connect prior knowledge and every-day experiences to physically acting out the meaning of words showing position. They further connect the physical movements to pictorial and symbolic representations. They communicate their understanding by describing what the word and the position means in relation to another physical object or a picture of an object. In kindergarten, language development and the development of mathematics go hand in hand. It is, therefore, important that children have concrete experiences to develop an understanding of the meaning of the words.

**Connections** Children make connections between language used in different subjects and mathematics. They also connect the language used in every-day life to the language in mathematics.

**Communication** Children communicate their understanding of the words describing position to their classmates and partners. They show the meaning of the words through their actions and by matching written words to the position of objects.

### Teaching Plan

**Materials** → Student pages 74–75; index cards; large teddy bear or other large stuffed toy; teddy bear counters

PLACE A TABLE or desk in the middle of the meeting area and have children gather in a large circle on the floor. The table should be large enough for children to crawl under but small enough for the teddy bear to climb over. Write the following words introduced in this lesson on index cards:

- under
- on
- beside
- below
- above

PRETEND THAT THE TEDDY BEAR in this activity talks to you. As you are holding the teddy bear up to your ear, tell the children that the teddy bear is telling you that he wants someone to put him under the table. *What does it mean to go under something?* Show the card with "under" written on it. Have children describe what going under a table means. A volunteer can then take the bear and place it under the table.

Have the child who is carrying the teddy bear stop under the table and stay seated. *Where are the teddy bear and (name of child) sitting?* Show the word "under" written on the index card. *What is above the teddy bear and (name of child)?* Show the word "above" to the children.

Have the child and the teddy bear come out from beneath the table. Again pretend that the teddy bear is telling you where he wants to go. Continue with the activity until all the vocabulary of the lesson has been introduced. Each time, have the children clarify what the newly introduced word means. Show the word to the children. After a child and the teddy bear follow the directions, have other children tell the position of the teddy bear and the child.

DO A QUICK REVIEW of the words and positions after all the words have been modeled. Place the teddy bear alone in each of these different positions in relation to the table. *Where is the teddy bear now?* The children's responses should be in relation to the table with answers such as, *"under the table,"* or *"over the table."*

Have the children return to their seats. Give each child a copy of student page 74 and a teddy bear counter. Have the children describe what they see on the page. They should articulate that they see a bed, a rocking chair, and a dresser.

**f.y.i.**

---

If you do not have teddy bear counters, use any other objects that are available and can easily be placed in the different positions by the children.

---

### What Might Happen . . . What to Do

Some children might find it difficult to describe some of these position words. They may need to act out rather than verbalize the meaning of the words. Although acting out the words is age-appropriate, ask children questions that will bring out the vocabulary. *What does it mean to be under something? How do you know when something is over you? If I were beside the table, where would I be?*

GIVE THE CHILDREN directions about where to place the teddy bear counter. These directions should include:

- on the bed
- under the bed
- beside the rocking chair
- above the dresser
- below the dresser.

Show the word written on the index cards with each direction.

If the children know how to read and write, encourage them to read and write the words they see on the index cards. They can also copy them on the student page after the directions.

AFTER THE CHILDREN HAVE PLACED the teddy bear counter in the different positions, have them draw the bear in one of the positions. They can share the positions with the class by describing where the bear is in relation to one of the pieces of furniture in the picture. If they are able, have them copy the position word below the picture of the bear.

Much of this lesson is based on language development and the experiences children have had in the past. If the children have not had previous experiences with these words, introduce only a few of them at a time and work on those until the children are comfortable with them. Introduce the rest of the words the following day or at a later date. Introduce only a few words at a time to children for whom English is a second language.

TO CONCLUDE THE LESSON, distribute student page 75. Before they begin the page, quickly review the position words introduced in the lesson. If children are not able to read the page, you may want to lead the class through the page.

## Student Pages

Student page 74 is used for the class activity. It shows a bedroom with a bed, a rocking chair, and a dresser or chest of drawers. Children are given directions for placing a teddy bear counter on the page. Student page 75 contains a matching activity in which children match a position word with the drawing that illustrates it.

## Assessment

As you observed children describing and acting out the position words, you were able to assess their understanding of the words. As they placed the teddy bear counter on the student page according to the directions you gave, you had further opportunity to assess their understanding of the words.

## NCTM Standards Summary

The children connected their everyday knowledge and prior experiences to acting out the positions in relation to a given object or picture. They communicated their understanding of what the words meant as they described each word. They further elaborated on the meanings of the words as they first acted out the directions, and then connected the physical activity to pictorial representations. Children also matched the written word to a drawing illustrating it, thus making further connections to symbolic representations.

**Answers**

*Page 74*
Answers will vary.

*Page 75*
1. under
2. on
3. beside
4. above

## Describing Positions in Space

**Listen to where the teddy bear wants to be. Place the bear there.**

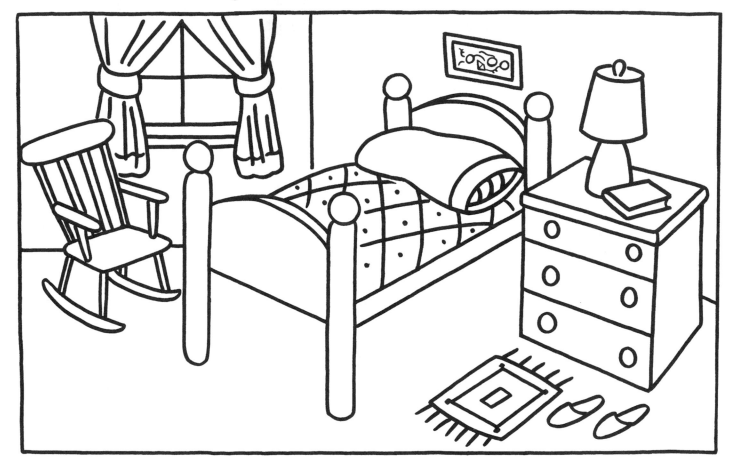

**Draw a picture of the bear on the bed.**

# Describing Positions in Space

**Where is the teddy bear? Draw a line from the word to the picture.**

| on | under | beside | above |
|----|-------|--------|-------|

❶

❷

❸

❹

# Recognizing Three-Dimensional Shapes

## Introduction

---

**Objective** → Children will recognize, describe, and name three-dimensional shapes.

**Context** → Children have worked with two-dimensional shapes in previous classroom activities. This is their first lesson on three-dimensional shapes. They will make connections between two-dimensional and three-dimensional shapes in future lessons.

## f.y.i.

---

To accomplish the lesson, it will be helpful to have several different size spheres, cylinders, cubes, and cones. You may wish to send a note home asking for parents to send in different objects so you will have enough.

## NCTM Standards Focus

Throughout this hands-on lesson, children formulate informal definitions of four three-dimensional shapes by observing their attributes. They also consider which attributes do and do not affect the definition of the shape. They use reasoning to determine whether or not a shape fits a definition. They look at shapes that have similar characteristics and determine whether they fit the definition of the shape.

**Connections** As children handle shapes, they make connections between what they see and feel and the shapes' characteristics. As they describe the shapes, they connect what they know about two-dimensional shapes and three-dimensional shapes.

**Communication** In class and small group discussions, children build a common vocabulary as they name the solids and describe their attributes. They are introduced to and use the correct names for the solids.

**Reasoning** Children use their reasoning skills to determine the classification of a particular shape.

## Teaching Plan

**Materials** → Student pages 80–81; chart paper; models of solids (cubes, cones, spheres, cylinders); classroom objects in the shapes of the solids

BEGIN THE LESSON by gathering children together. Tell them that they will be learning about shapes that take up space, shapes they can actually hold. Take a few minutes to talk about the general characteristics of three-dimensional shapes. Then hold up several different-sized spheres for the children to see. Pass the spheres among the children. Tell the children to study the spheres and then to describe them. Children may use the name of an object, such as "ball" to describe it. Ask how all these spheres are alike. Encourage children to use attributes such as round and curved. Record what children say so you can start getting a definition of a sphere on chart paper. Either draw or paste a picture of the object next to its description.

Gather the spheres together and again ask how they are the same. Also ask how they are different. For differences, children may mention size and color. Ask them to think about the spheres and to decide which descriptions are the "important ones." Children should see that size, color, and the material a sphere is made of do not determine whether or not an object is a sphere. As children explore other shapes, continue to ask about what descriptons do and do not affect a shape's classification.

---

**What Might Happen . . . What to Do**

Children might have a difficult time saying much about a sphere other than it is round. However, one of the key characteristics of a sphere is that every point on its surface is the same distance from the center of the sphere. Children may refer to this as "perfectly round." To help children grasp this idea, you might show them an object such as a football, that has rounded surfaces but is not a sphere and have them compare the object to a sphere.

---

Continue the lesson by having children explore and describe each of the other shapes. Below is a list of some features that children should mention. Focus on the shapes of the sides. Discuss the number of sides, or *faces*. Talk about whether sides are flat or rounded. Have children examine the number of corners or points. Remind children that size, color, and material are not important.

**Cube**

- It has six sides that are all the same size.
- The sides are flat.
- It has eight corners and they are all square.

You may wish to show children a rectangular prism that is not a cube, such as a cereal box. Make sure they talk about why it is not a cube.

**Cylinder**

- It has two flat ends that are circles.
- It rolls.
- Its middle is rounded. It can stand on either end.

Compare a cylinder to a cone.

**Cone**

- It has one flat end that is a circle.
- It has one end that is a point.
- The side is rounded and is biggest at the circle end.

A pyramid is a good shape to compare with a cone. You can also use a cylinder.

The following two activities can either be done as part of this lesson or over the next several days. Both activities can be done many times and will help children remember the names of the shapes and their characteristics.

## Activity 1: Guess My Shape

Give each child a copy of student page 80 and have children cut along the dotted lines. If you have enough three-dimensional blocks of each figure, you may want children to use them instead. Have children put the shapes in front of themselves. Give clues, one at a time, about a shape. When possible make the first clue one that can apply to several figures. For example, *I have more than one face.* Tell children to turn the picture over when think they know the shape. When you have given all the clues ask children to show the picture of the shape.

Here is an example of a set of clues.

*I have a circle.*

*I can stand up only on one end.*

*I have a point.*

*Who am I?* (cone)

## Activity 2: Shape Story

Have children make up and illustrate a shape story. Ask them to pretend that they are going on a trip and that they are going to take some shapes with them. Have the class decide which shapes they are going to take along. They can take as many as they want. Then as you write it on the board or on chart paper, have the children make up a story about the shapes. At least some of the adventures that happen to the shapes should be based on their characteristics. For example, if the children take a sphere, they might try to put it on a surface that it rolls off of.

To conclude the lesson, distribute copies of student page 81. Have the class work through the page as you read the instructions.

## Student Pages

Student page 80 has pictures of shapes that can be cut out and used for the "Guess My Shape" activity. Student page 81 has pictures of shapes for children to identify.

## Assessment

As you listened to the children's descriptions of the shapes, you had an opportunity to find out what children considered important features of each shape. You were able to assess the children's understanding of the essential characteristics of the shapes as they described the shapes and as they completed student page 81.

## NCTM Standards Summary

Children made connections between shapes and their characteristics as they named and described four three-dimensional shapes. They communicated their observations as they handled the shapes. Children were also asked why certain shapes that had similar features to known shapes did not fit the definition of that shape. This was an informal way of beginning to have children look at counter examples.

**Answer**

*Page 80*
There are no answers.

*Page 81*
Check children's work.

# Recognizing Three-Dimensional Shapes

**Use these shapes for Guess My Shape.**

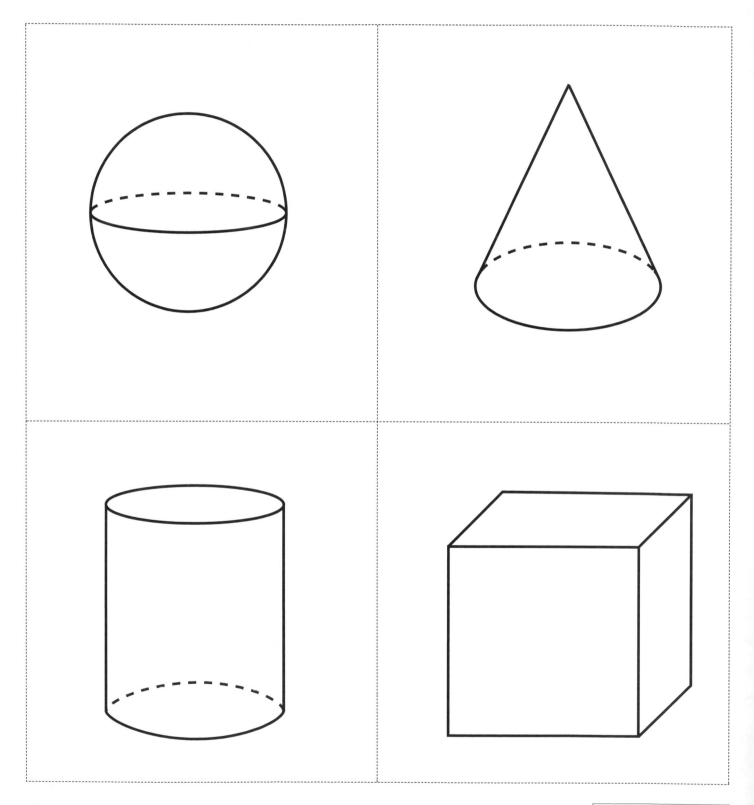

# Recognizing Three-Dimensional Shapes

**1** Make an x on the cube.

**2** Draw a ring around the cylinder.

**3** Draw a box around the sphere.

**4** Draw a line under the cone.

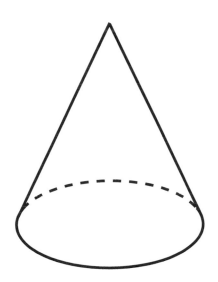

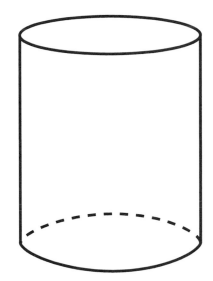

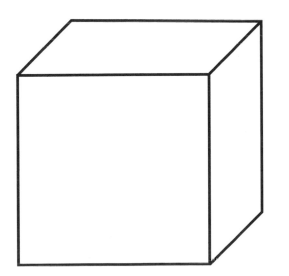

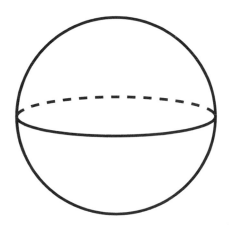

# Relating Two- and Three- Dimensional Shapes

## Introduction

**Objective** → Children will recognize, name, describe, and match the faces of three-dimensional shapes to the two-dimensional shapes.

**Context** → Children have explored two- and three-dimensional shapes. They can recognize, name, and describe the attributes of shapes. They will continue to explore the relationships of two- and three-dimensional shapes.

## NCTM Standards Focus

In this standards-based lesson, children name the three-dimensional shapes, and as they handle the shapes physically, they communicate to the class as many attributes of the shape as they can think of. This lesson is unusual, because children then create visual pictures of the different faces that make up the three-dimensional shapes. They then rely on these pictures to draw conclusions about which shape might best relate to the two-dimensional shapes they encounter.

**Reasoning and Proof** Children draw conclusions about three-dimensional shapes by observing shadows cast from an overhead that are two-dimensional representations from parts of the shapes. They reason their conclusions from the attributes or visual pictures they have of the different solids and conclude which three-dimensional shape it might be.

**Connections** Children make connections between their knowledge of two- and three-dimensional shapes to decide which three-dimensional shape the two-dimensional representations might relate to.

**Communication** Children recognize, describe, and name two- and three-dimensional shapes. They relate their observations to each other and explain their thinking. After completing the student page, they again share with the class and explain why and how they made their decisions.

## Teaching Plan

**Materials** → Student pages 86–87; three-dimensional solids—cube, cone, cylinder, sphere; chart paper; overhead projector; a small divider such as a folder

DISTRIBUTE THE SOLIDS one at a time among the children. Have them handle the shapes, before asking them to name each one. After they have named the shape, have them describe the shape and its attributes. Record each shape on chart paper and list the attributes the children suggest.

Begin with the sphere and follow with the cube, the cone, and the cylinder. If children use incorrect terminology or names such as circle or ball for sphere, box or square for cube, and hat or ice-cream cone for cone, introduce the correct mathematical terms.

PLAY THE FOLLOWING GAME with the children. Place a cube on the overhead projector but be sure to hide the actual shape from the children's view with a folder or a small divider. Have children guess which shape you have placed on the overhead. Once the children have made their guesses, have them tell why they think that is the shape. Encourage children to use as many attributes of the shape/shapes that they think it is.

Have children refer back to the chart with the lists of attributes for each shape. Remove the folder that is hiding the shape. Have children tell which part of the three-dimensional shape they were seeing. *Do you think you will see the same shape if I pick this up and place it in a different way on the overhead?*

While children are discussing the different possibilities, make sure they refer to the shadow that is made on the overhead. Have children tell why the shadows are the same or different. Encourage them to generalize why the cube or the sphere always casts the same shadow regardless of how it is placed. On the other hand, ask them to consider why the shadows of the cone and cylinder appear different when the figure is placed differently on the overhead.

PLACE A CONE base-down on the overhead. Ask children to guess which shape it might be. Since the shadow will be a circle, the children might guess that it is a cone, a sphere, or a cylinder. If there is no significant difference between the diameters of these three shapes, it will be difficult for the children to determine which shape it is.

Discuss with children what else they need to see in order to determine which three-dimensional shape it is. They should ask to see the shadow of the "side" of the shape, before they can tell for sure which shape they are dealing with. Have them tell why seeing the side of the shape will help them. They should volunteer the different attributes of the three shapes.

If there is a significant difference between the diameters, children should be able to determine which shape it is by comparing size. They should include this attribute in their discussion and ask to see the shadow of the other two shapes that will give a circular shadow.

**f.y.i.**

-----------------------------------------

If this is the first lesson that the children have had on three-dimensional shapes or they need more time, allow them ample time to explore the shapes before continuing the lesson. Have them hold and describe each shape in depth. You might also have children look around the room to see what everyday objects have a similar shape. You may want to ask children what things at home are made up of these shapes. Have them draw pictures of the things and share them with the class.

## What Might Happen . . . What to Do

Some children might find it difficult to predict which shape is on the overhead projector, because they have not had enough experiences with three-dimensional shapes. Keep a set of the four three-dimensional shapes in front of the children as you show the shadows on the overhead. Encourage children to handle the shapes and as they predict which shape it is on the overhead, have them tell why and what made them decide on that shape.

DISTRIBUTE STUDENT PAGE 86 to the children. Have them match the pictures of the solids to the shadows from the overhead or the two-dimensional shapes shown on the page. Tell them to think about why they made these matches, and have them share their thoughts with the class.

When all the children are finished, call on different children to summarize the activity and to share how they solved the problems on the student page. Ask them to explain what made them match the shapes the way they did. Have them explain what part of the three-dimensional shape matches the shadow pictures in the different quadrants.

Encourage children to use the solids in the classroom to prove their answers. Ask them to show the solid they are talking about. Have them show the face or faces of this solid that are depicted as shadow pictures. Ask them to describe the two-dimensional shape that is depicted and how they see it on the solid. They need to show that both of these shapes have similarities.

You may wish to have the following center activity. Make a card that shows the shadow or a face for one of the four figures. On the back make a drawing of the figure the shadow could come from. For some drawings you may need to show several figures. For example, for a circle you would need to show the cone, cylinder, and sphere. Place the cards, shadow side up by the actual figures. Have children take a card and select the figures that match a card. Then they can check their work.

## Student Pages

Student page 86 is used for the class activity. It shows shadows from each of the four three-dimensional shapes that are drawn at the bottom of the page. Children match the solid and its name to its shadow picture. Student page 87 can be used as homework. Children draw pictures of two things that look like any of the solids.

## Assessment

As the children responded to the questions asked in the lesson, you assessed their correct use of geometric terminology. You observed the children as they matched the shadow parts of the four solids to a particular solid. As children told why the shadow pictures matched the solids, you evaluated their understanding of how the two-dimensional shapes identified the three-dimensional shapes.

## NCTM Standards Summary

Children communicated their understanding and knowledge of three-dimensional shapes as they made connections between two- and three-dimensional shapes. They used the attributes of the two-dimensional shapes to reason which three-dimensional shape might be depicted. They related the attributes of the three-dimensional shapes to the two-dimensional shapes as they were proving how they were connected. Children explained their thinking as they communicated the relationship that exists between the two-dimensional shapes and the three-dimensional shapes.

**Answers**

*Page 86*
1. Cone
2. Sphere
3. Cube

*Page 87*
1–2. Answers will vary.

# Relating Two- and Three-Dimensional Shapes

**Match the shapes to the shadow pictures.**

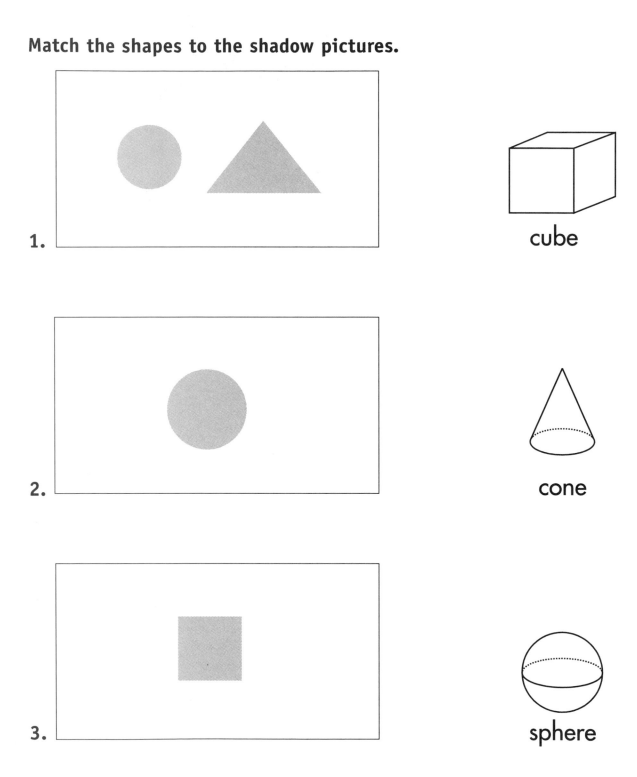

# Relating Two- and Three-Dimensional Shapes

**Look at the shapes on the page.**
**Find two things that look like any of the shapes.**
**Draw a picture of the two things you found.**

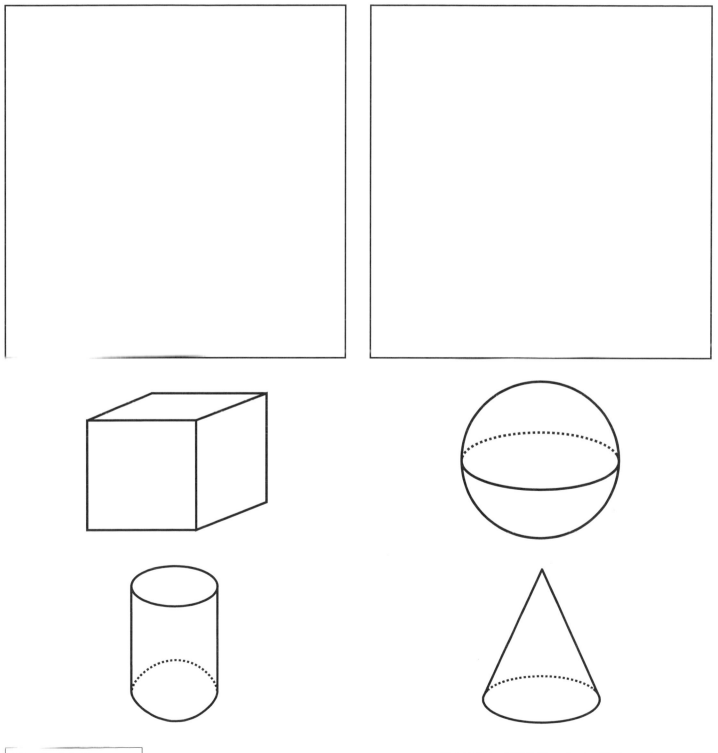

# Investigating Circles and Squares

## Introduction

------------------------------------

**Objective** → Children will identify objects shaped like circles and squares.

**Context** → This lesson takes place at the beginning of a unit on geometry. Follow-up lessons may include identifying objects shaped like rectangles, triangles, spheres, and cubes.

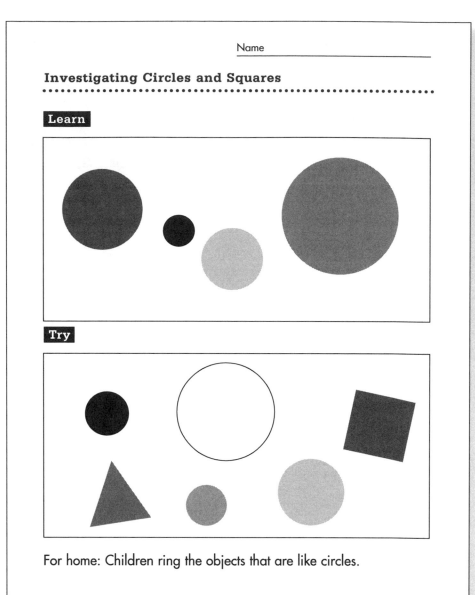

Name _____

**Investigating Circles and Squares**
••••••••••••••••••••••••••••••••••••••••••••••••••••

**Learn**

**Try**

For home: Children ring the objects that are like circles.

## NCTM Process Standards Analysis and Focus

The standards analysis examines how the process standards have been incorporated into the above lesson. By increasing the focus on three of the process standards, a more effective and meaningful lesson can be presented. The suggestions offered can help you to think about how this might be accomplished.

**Reasoning and Proof** Throughout the lesson, children are asked to name and identify shapes, but they are not asked to explain how they recognize those shapes. Accompanying notes suggest that the teacher present different-size squares and circles for children to sort.

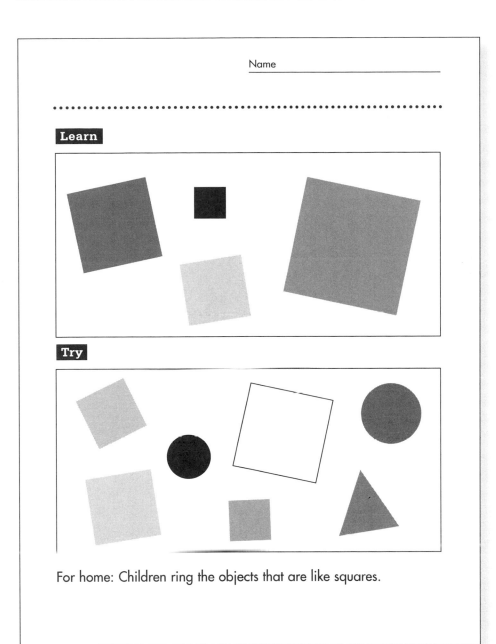

Name _____

**Learn**

**Try**

For home: Children ring the objects that are like squares.

*Suggestion* → Plan activities for children to analyze attributes of circles and squares. Comparing circles with other closed curves will help children to visualize similarities and differences. Incorporate similar activities to develop children's understanding of what distinguishes squares from other polygons. Reinforce children's understanding by having them explain which shapes are circles or squares and why.

**Representation** Children are asked to identify geometric shapes and representations of familiar objects on activity pages.

*Suggestion* → Have children locate objects in the classroom, around the neighborhood, and at home that represent circles and squares. Involving children in experiences such as building models, creating pictures, and sorting shapes will help them to recognize the specific attributes of circles and squares.

**Communication** Children are asked to identify shapes with questions that elicit one-word responses; they are not asked to explain how they know.

*Suggestion* → Organize learning experiences that encourage children to share their ideas and clarify their thinking. Have children discuss attributes of squares and circles as they compare different shapes. These opportunities will allow children to confirm shape recognition, increase their understanding of terms, and develop appropriate language for describing shapes.

**Problem Solving** Given that the focus of the lesson is shape recognition, there is not much opportunity for problem solving.

**Connections** An activity referenced in the accompanying notes encourages children to look around the classroom to find objects shaped like circles or squares.

The teaching plan that follows shows how the suggestions for increasing the focus on the process standards can be implemented.

## Revised Teaching Plan

**Materials** → Large circle and square; chart paper; string; shape templates; sponges; paint, crayons

Disrupt a large circle. *Who knows what we call this shape?* Most children will easily identify the shape as a circle. Repeat the name of the shape for reinforcement. *How can we describe a circle?* (It's round.) Now display a small circle. *Is this a circle? How do you know?*

Next, display or draw an oval. *What about this shape? Is this a circle? Why or why not?* Children should be able to describe the oval as looking like a stretched-out circle or like an egg. If necessary, have children trace the shape to help generate words that describe it. Tactile experiences will enhance and strengthen the learning experience. Using a piece of string, show children that for a given circle, you can stretch the string from one side of the circumference through the center to the other side and always use the same length of string. Repeat this with an oval. Children should see that the length of string varies as you stretch it across the shape.

Invite children to identify circular objects in the classroom. List and illustrate children's responses on chart paper. Have children look at the chart again and compare the shape of each object with the first circle you displayed. *Are these both round? Are these both the same shape? Are they both circles?* These questions help children focus on specific attributes of circles. As children compare classroom objects to the original circle shape, they begin to recognize specific properties of circles.

Repeat the same activities to investigate squares. Take time to discuss specific details of squares as you present the shape. Draw children's attention to the number of corners and sides. Help them to see how a square has 4 sides and 4 corners and that all sides are the same length. Extend the activity to compare squares with rectangles, triangles, pentagons, and other polygons. Encourage children to handle concrete models to allow them to experience attributes of the shapes tactilely.

### f.y.i.

-----------------------------------

Measure the length of one side of a square using string or a marked piece of paper. Use this measure to demonstrate how all sides of the square are the same length. This will reinforce children's understanding that all sides of a square are equal to one another.

ORGANIZE SMALL-GROUP LEARNING ACTIVITIES to reinforce children's understandings of shapes and their characteristics. Select from activities below to explore the concept in a variety of contexts. Rotate the activities throughout your day or week according to your schedule.

**Activity 1** Plan a shape walk around the school. Encourage children to look for objects that are circular and/or square in shape. When you return to the classroom, help children write a language-experience story to describe the shapes they saw. Invite volunteers to illustrate some of the shapes. Then as a follow-up, ask children to find things at home to add to the story. Use these experiences to build on what children already know about shapes and expand their knowledge base.

## What Might Happen . . . What to Do

Some children may find it difficult to see shapes in real-world objects. On your walk, have children work in pairs. Give each pair a circle and square shape to use as a reference. Encourage partners to compare objects they see on their walk with their circle and square shapes.

**Activity 2** Provide templates of circles and squares that children can use to create patterns. Model how to trace the shapes on paper with a crayon. Allow time for children to describe their patterns. Place their patterns in an activity center for others to match and extend. As children create their patterns, they are actively examining the attributes of each shape. Tracing activities reinforce the attributes of each shape.

**Activity 3** Cut sponges into circle and square shapes. Make a variety of sizes for each shape. Show children how to place the sponge in paint to make prints and have children use the shapes to make colorful pictures. Then have children dictate a sentence that describes the shapes used in their picture. Writing opportunities help children to organize their thinking and provide another way to exercise understanding. Display the completed pictures around the room.

**Activity 4** Assign children to small groups. Hold a square or circle high in the air for all groups to see. Then have children work in their groups to form the shape with their bodies. Remind children to discuss each shape's attributes before they begin to form it. Encourage children to consider different ways to make the shapes, such as standing up and holding hands or lying down on the ground.

**Activity 5** Provide materials such as yarn and glue, or toothpicks and play dough, for children to use to create circles and squares. Then help children to label their shapes. Finally, allow time for children to talk about and describe their shapes before displaying them around the classroom.

## f.y.i.

------------------------------------

To extend the sorting activity, include pictures of real-world objects that you have cut from magazines and laminated for durability.

**Activity 6** Create shape-sorting mats. Draw a circle and a square at the top of each mat. Place a variety of shapes in a box for children to sort. Make sure there are shapes of different colors and sizes. If necessary, demonstrate how to compare shapes from the box with the images at the top of the mat. Listen and observe as children complete the sorting activity. Encourage children to explain their sorting strategies to the class.

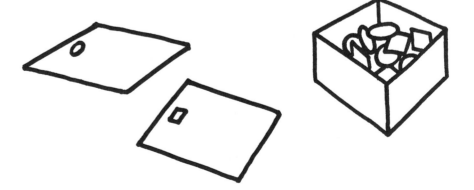

**Activity 7** Play the game "I Spy." Give children a few clues about an object in the classroom such as a box of crackers. *I spy something in this room. It has four corners and four sides. It's red and white. It's near the window.* The person who correctly guesses the object begins the next round of clues.

INCORPORATE ACTIVITIES AND GAMES throughout the day that encourage children to think about shape attributes.

## Student Pages

Children should now be ready to complete exercises similar to those on the reduced student pages.

## Assessment

Children's pictures and models offered insight about their developing knowledge of shapes. Their drawings and dictated sentences provided a pictorial representation along with written reflections of their thinking. Children's ability to analyze characteristics and define properties of shapes could be assessed as they formed and sorted shapes.

## NCTM Standards Summary

A wide range of learning experiences allowed children to analyze and define the characteristics of circles and squares. The variety of activities helped children to build and extend their knowledge about these shapes. Manipulatives and art materials were used to provide opportunities to represent shapes. Children were able to build, draw, describe, compare, and sort shapes in a variety of contexts. Sorting and tracing shapes gave children time to look for and talk about attributes. All of these activities also provided a rich context for children to hear and use the language of mathematics to describe shapes.

# Standard 4 **Measurement**

**A**T THE KINDERGARTEN LEVEL, measurement includes a lot of work with various aspects of length, weight, and height. Our lessons are derived from these important topics, and include a lesson on arranging objects from shortest to tallest, a lesson on comparing weights using appropriate vocabulary, a lesson on measuring length using nonstandard units, and a lesson on comparing lengths using appropriate vocabulary.

Three lessons model how the process standards can be used to teach content. A fourth lesson is a hypothetical textbook lesson that we have revised to be more standards based. These four lessons do not represent the entire curriculum, but rather provide glimpses of how, with a more concentrated effort to incorporate the process standards, better mathematics teaching and learning can be achieved.

One lesson we have chosen has children arrange objects from shortest to tallest. By incorporating the process standards of problem solving and communication, children develop strategies for arranging three or more objects by height, and develop the vocabulary to describe the objects appropriately in comparison to one another.

Another lesson we have chosen is one in which children compare weights of objects using appropriate vocabulary. Children are often shown balances and told that the heavier side is lower. This lesson has children hold objects for themselves and make connections to the vocabulary. Communication is also an emphasis here as children learn and use new vocabulary, and teachers use good questioning to lead children to important conclusions. Children use reasoning to discover that larger does not necessarily mean heavier.

A third lesson we have chosen is one that has children measure length using nonstandard units. Children are presented with problem-solving situations in which they choose their own units to measure certain lengths. Children use communication to discuss their methods for measuring, and they begin to understand how different-sized units affect measurements.

The hypothetical textbook lesson that we have chosen to revise has children compare lengths. Through increased emphasis on reasoning and proof, communication, and representation, children will have more chances to learn and use appropriate vocabulary, and to realize that objects must be measured from the same baseline.

## Standard 4 Lessons

**Arranging Shortest to Tallest**

**Comparing Weights**

**Exploring Length**

**Comparing Lengths**

# Arranging Shortest to Tallest

## Introduction

----------------------------------------

**Objective** → Children will compare and order objects by height.

**Context** → Children will have had experiences with sorting objects into groups. Children will continue to have experiences with comparing, sorting, ordering, and describing objects by measurable attributes such as length, weight, and area.

## NCTM Standards Focus

In this lesson, children build on their experiences with comparing and sorting to order objects by height. This is a challenging task because it requires children to consider relationships among three or more objects so they can order them correctly. By focusing on the process standards, this lesson enables children to develop their own strategies and to apply them. The lesson also helps establish the expectation that sharing one's thinking about mathematics is part of doing math.

**Problem Solving** Children develop strategies to order objects by height. They apply their strategies to new situations.

**Communication** Children use mathematical vocabulary to describe the qualitative relationships they see. They use terms such as taller, tallest, shorter, and shortest appropriately.

## Teaching Plan

**Materials** → Student pages 100–101; objects of varying heights (boxes, cans, blocks, etc.); drawing paper; crayons or markers; scissors; glue

**Preparation** → Place 5 objects of varying heights on each table.

GATHER THE CLASS TOGETHER. Ask three children of different heights to stand side by side in front of the group. Arrange them from shortest to tallest. *How do you think I arranged these friends?* Accept the children's responses. To guide them to consider height, select two more children: *Where will [child's name] fit in the row? Why do you think so?*

Encourage children to explain that their classmates are ordered from shortest to tallest, or by height. *Who is shorter than [child's name]? Who is taller than [child's name]? Who is the tallest?*

One by one, invite three more children to place themselves where they belong in the row. Encourage the rest of the class to decide if each person is in the correct place and to tell why. Talk about the words *tall, taller, tallest,* and *short, shorter, shortest,* and use them in your questions.

NEXT, HAVE GROUPS OF CHILDREN go to the tables where you have placed the five objects. Explain that they are going to work with their group to put the objects in order from the shortest to the tallest. Everyone in the group should agree on the order. If someone doesn't agree, ask the person to explain why, and see if you can come to an agreement. This fosters good communication among children, speaking and listening to each other. This allows children to use the new vocabulary.

As you circulate among the children, ask questions such as the following: *How did you know where to put this object? Which object is the tallest? How do you know? How does the order of the objects show that? Does it matter which object is the widest or narrowest? Why or why not?*

Once the children agree on the order of the objects, have each child draw a picture to show how he or she arranged the objects by height. As the children complete their drawings, encourage them to visit other tables to see how other groups arranged their objects.

**f.y.i.**

------------------------------------

Have all the children face the objects you want them to compare. They should all sit on the same side of the table so they can agree that, for example, the shortest object is the first on the left.

---

## What Might Happen . . . What to Do

------------------------------------------------------------------------

Some children might have difficulty considering all 5 objects at the same time. Help the children to compare 2 or 3 objects at first, then work in the other objects one at a time.

---

FINALLY, BRING EVERYONE TOGETHER to talk about their work. Ask questions that focus children's attention on the strategies they used. *How did you decide where to place your objects?* You can reinforce ordinal numbers and encourage children to think and talk about their methods by asking: *How did you know which object would be first (second, third)?* You can also ask which attributes are relevant to the problem. *Did it matter that one object was wider than the others? Why or why not?*

## What Might Happen . . . What to Do

Children's drawings might reflect that they are not aware of the need to measure from the same baseline. Hold up 2 vertical objects (such as wooden blocks or sticks of chalk) of different lengths, aligned at the base. Ask the children which block is taller, and how they know. Then hold up the blocks again, without aligning them, so the top of the shorter block is higher. Again, ask children which block is taller, and how they know. Some might immediately recognize that the blocks are not aligned, and that the shorter item is still shorter. Others may identify the shorter block as taller. Discuss this conflict. *How could it be that this block was shorter and is now taller?* Some young children may need more experiences with comparing heights of objects before they are able to recognize or resolve this conflict.

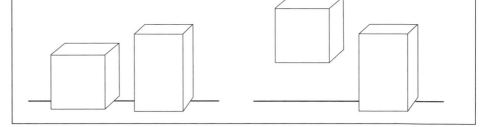

Have children do student pages 100 and 101. Read the directions aloud to the children. When they have finished, have them discuss their work, using the kind of questioning you used to discuss the objects.

## Student Pages

Page 100 gives children 5 houses to cut out. Page 101 asks children to arrange the houses from shortest to tallest and paste them along a street.

## Assessment

This lesson offered opportunities to assess children's ability to develop strategies for ordering objects. As they moved from arranging their classmates and objects in order to working on the student pages, you could determine if they applied their strategies to new situations. You were also able to assess their understanding of comparative measurement terms. You could note whether they used vocabulary correctly when they shared their work and whether they applied the vocabulary to new situations.

## NCTM Standards Summary

In this lesson, children investigated the attribute of height within a problem-solving situation. They visually and physically compared the heights of objects in order to arrange the objects by height. Children were encouraged to develop their own strategies for ordering objects from shortest to tallest, and to note and describe the relevant attributes of the objects. In groups and whole-class discussion, children communicated their thinking as they shared their strategies and used measurement vocabulary such as taller, tallest, shorter, and shortest.

**Answers**

*Page 101*
Houses should be in order from shortest to tallest and should be aligned on the baseline.

# Arranging Shortest to Tallest

**Cut out each house.**

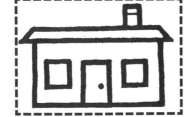

Standard 4 Measurement

# Arranging Shortest to Tallest

**Put the houses in order from shortest to tallest.**
**Glue the houses in order on the street.**

# Comparing Weights

## Introduction

------------------------------------

**Objective** → Children will understand the terms *light, heavy, lighter,* and *heavier*. They will understand that *light* and *heavy* are not affected by size.

**Context** → Most children begin school with some intuitive understanding of the concept of weight. Children will continue having experiences comparing the weights of objects, and in future grades will use standard units of measure to describe weight.

## NCTM Standards Focus

Children are often asked to distinguish between lighter and heavier objects by looking at balances and realizing that the heavier side is lower than the lighter side. A more standards-based lesson would give children the opportunity to compare weights of objects for themselves. By incorporating the following process standards, children will better understand the comparison of lighter versus heavier.

**Connections** Children will connect weight with how heavy an object feels rather than its size. Connections will also be made between tactile experiences and vocabulary.

**Reasoning and Proof** Children will handle uniform-looking items and compare their weights. They will place items in order by weight and explain how they made their decision.

**Communication** Children will use appropriate vocabulary to express comparative weights of objects.

## Teaching Plan

**Materials** → Student pages 106–107; identical yogurt cups (or other identical nontransparent containers) with lids, 4 per table; 4 kinds of filler materials with distinctly different weights (e.g., foam packing material, cotton balls, macaroni, multi-link cubes, rice, sand, pebbles); heavy wooden block; sheet of paper; chart paper; heavy book; 2 boxes with lids, 1 large enough to hold the heavy book, the other visibly larger

**Preparation** → Fill the 4 yogurt cups in each set with 4 different fillers. Then label each set uniformly so, for example, the cotton balls are in B, the macaroni in D, the rice in C, and the pebbles in A. Prepare 1 set of mystery containers for each table. Put the heavy book in the smaller box, and fill the larger box with lightweight packing material such as styrofoam peanuts. Close the boxes.

GATHER THE CHILDREN in a circle. Show them a heavy object, such as a wooden block, and a light object, such as a piece of paper. Pass both objects around the circle, so that each child holds them for a moment. As the objects are being passed, ask children to describe the objects and their observations about them.

After all the children have had a chance to hold the objects, continue the lesson by asking these questions: *How would you describe the weight of the block as compared to the weight of the paper? How would you describe the weight of the paper as compared to the weight of the block?* Notice how the questions focus the children on the one attribute that you want them to discuss. Record their words on chart paper.

*How can you tell whether something is heavy or light?* Discuss the children's ideas. Some may say, "You can tell by how it feels when you hold it" or suggest weighing the objects. Others may link weight to size, explaining that the block is heavier because it is bigger.

DISCUSS WITH THE CHILDREN whether you can tell how heavy something is by how big it is. Ask them to think of some large things that are heavy and some large things that are light. (A large dog, an empty trash can) Then ask about small things that are light and small things that are heavy. (A cotton ball, a rock)

Introduce the two prepared boxes. Explain that these are mystery boxes. Engage children's reasoning skills by asking questions. *Can you tell which box is heavier? Why or why not? Without lifting the boxes, can you tell which box is heavier?* Record their observations on the board or on chart paper.

**What Children Might Say**

- Yes—the bigger box must be heavier.
- No—a heavier object could be in the smaller box.
- No—can't tell without lifting.

## What Might Happen . . . What to Do

For some children, the visual attribute of size can be very compelling. They might insist that the larger the object, the heavier it must be. Discuss that while seeing the size of an object can sometimes give us information about how heavy it is, our sense of feel is what we use to compare weights. Provide children more opportunities to compare objects that are large and heavy, large and light, small and heavy, and small and light.

**f.y.i.**

If you wish, read aloud the story *When This Box Is Full*, by Patricia Lillie with illustrations by Donald Crews. You may want to continue this lesson on the following day. To close this part of the lesson, have children write about or draw what they would put in each mystery box.

## f.y.i.

----------------------------------------

For children who are learning to speak English, this lesson may be challenging because of the terms *light, lighter, lightest,* and *heavy, heavier, heaviest.* Some children who understand the concept of comparing weight may have difficulty with these words. Using exactly the same size and type of containers (for instance, identical yogurt cups) will help them focus on the only difference between the containers—their weight.

Distribute student page 106 and explain that children will compare objects and record their work. Read the directions aloud to the children. Have them share their completed drawings and their experiences. *What objects were hard to compare? What objects were easy to compare? Did you have some objects that seemed to weigh the same?*

BRING THE GROUP TOGETHER and show the children one set of yogurt containers. Ask children to describe the mystery containers without touching them. Make sure they note that the containers are the same size and shape, and each is labeled with a letter.

Ask about the weights of the containers. *Are some of these containers heavier than others? Can you tell just by looking?* Some children may guess at the relative weights of the containers. Others may say that since they are all the same size, they must all be the same weight. Explain that some of the mystery containers are heavier than others.

Tell children that they will work in groups. Each table will get a set of mystery containers. They can pick up the containers and see how they feel. Each group should decide which container is the lightest and which is the heaviest. Then they should put the containers in order from lightest to heaviest. Everyone at the table should agree on the order. When they have finished, each group will share their work with the class.

WHEN EVERYONE HAS FINISHED, invite groups to share their work. Each group should explain how they decided whether one container was heavier than another and how they finally put the four containers in order. Encourage children to ask questions to make sure they understand the strategy and results. Record the final order for each group on chart paper.

After all groups have shared, compare their results on the chart paper. *Did some of the groups put the containers in different orders? Why might that be?* Talk about the idea that when objects are close in weight, it can be hard to know for sure which one is heavier.

## Extension

Some children may have had previous experiences with comparing objects by weight, and they may be ready for more of a challenge. Introduce the pan balance as a means of comparing weight. Place a yogurt container on each side of the balance, and ask the children to describe what happens. Connect the order children gave the weights of the containers with the position of the balance. *Why does one side of the balance move down and the other up? What would happen if we put two objects that are exactly the same weight on the sides of the balance?* Have children place different objects on the balance and talk about which is heavier and which is lighter, and how they know. Guide the children to conclude that the heavier object lowers the pan of the balance.

## Student Pages

Student page 106 has children compare the weight of a book to other objects in the classroom. Student page 107 asks children to compare and record the weights of two objects at home.

## Assessment

This lesson provided opportunities to assess the children's understanding of weight and the words used to describe it. Children explored the idea that how an object feels gives more information than how it looks. Children's discussion of this idea offered some insight into whether they were able to disregard size, even when it seemed to be a compelling attribute, and focus on weight. The mystery container activity showed whether children could arrange four identical-looking objects by weight.

## NCTM Standards Summary

In this lesson, children made connections to their own experiences with weight and size. They used reasoning and proof to consider whether size and weight were directly related (whether larger means heavier). Children used the vocabulary of this lesson to communicate with each other about how to arrange a group of containers in order from lightest to heaviest.

**Answers**

Answers to student pages 106–107 will vary.

## Comparing Weights

**Get a book from your classroom library.**
**Find 2 things that are heavier than the book. Draw the 2 things here.**

**Find 2 things that are lighter than the book. Draw the 2 things here.**

Standard 4 Measurement

## Comparing Weights

**Find 2 things in your house.**
**Which is heavier? Draw it here.**

**Which thing is lighter? Draw it here.**

# Exploring Length

## Introduction

------------------------------------

**Objective** → Children will measure length using nonstandard units.

**Context** → Kindergarten children have had experiences comparing lengths. In future lessons, they will continue to measure with nonstandard units to quantify and compare lengths, and measure using a ruler.

## NCTM Standards Focus

Often children are asked to measure by counting units that are laid out for them. In this standards-based lesson, children choose nonstandard units to measure length and then work out ways to make the actual measurements. Through hands-on experience and group discussion, they develop their understanding not only of measurement, but also of addition and number.

**Problem Solving** As children measure and compare results, they encounter important problem-solving situations. They also apply their measuring skills to solve problems.

**Communication** Children discuss their methods of measuring. As they report and compare their results, they begin to understand how measurement helps us communicate with each other about length and distance.

## Teaching Plan

**Materials** → Student pages 112–113; colored plastic tape; picture or drawing of a tree with a beehive; picture or drawing of a house; a long block or length of ribbon; craft sticks or 4-inch paper strips; scissors

**Preparation** → Place several strips of tape 12 to 16 feet long on the floor in the classroom, hall, or gym. The paths should differ in length. Place one strip of tape in the classroom meeting area to be used for discussion. Put the house drawing at one end of the path, and the tree at the other end.

GATHER THE CHILDREN TOGETHER in the classroom meeting area. *Have you ever put things end-to-end to find out how long something is?* As the children share what they've done, note how each child explains the process of measuring. Show a long block or a length of ribbon and ask how you could find the length of the block. *What things could I put end-to-end along the block?*

Good communication involves asking children questions that help them to clarify their own thinking. *Where does the first measuring unit have to be placed?* (At one end of the object to be measured) *Is it important to lay the measuring units end-to-end? Why or why not?* (Yes. If there were gaps, some of the length would not be measured. If the units overlapped, some of the length would be measured twice.)

ENCOURAGE CHILDREN TO FIND OBJECTS in the classroom that would work for measuring the block. Ask them to describe what they would do. They may suggest, for example, lining up connecting cubes along the block and then counting the number of cubes used. Have them carry out their plan. As they work, look for the methods they use. When they have finished, ask them to discuss their work. Listen for vocabulary words that reflect an understanding of the process.

---

### What Might Happen . . . What to Do

Some children might have difficulty choosing appropriate materials for measuring length. Guide them to choose materials that are significantly longer than they are wide, such as straws, paper clips, or craft sticks. Explain that, in order to say how long something is, we use items of the same kind. So rather than measuring with a combination of craft sticks, straws, and paper clips, we choose one unit so we can say that the block is 8 paper clips long.

---

TELL THIS STORY to introduce a problem-solving situation in which nonstandard measurement of length can be used.

> One morning Bear got up from his warm bed, and as usual he was hungry. It was time for breakfast! So Bear picked up his honey pot and set off down the path to his favorite tree to get some honey, just as he did every morning. As he walked along, Bear thought, "Hmmm, I walk to my favorite tree every morning to get my honey. I wonder how long the path from my house to my tree is." But Bear didn't know how to find out.

Show children the path you taped to the floor with the house and tree at the ends. Ask them to imagine that this is the path Bear walks every morning. *What do you think Bear could do to find out how long the path is from his house to the honey tree?*

Let children share their ideas. You might want to let children model one of the suggestions. For example, craft sticks can be lined up end-to-end along the path, and the number of craft sticks could be counted.

Tell the children that Bear thought he might use his footprints (or paw prints), and that you have a copy of Bear's footprint for each child. *How*

### f.y.i.

---

You might want to cut out the paw prints yourself so the length is more uniform. Also, you might want to reproduce the paw prints on a sturdier paper so they can be reused.

*could you use Bear's footprints to measure this path?* Once the children suggest laying the footprints end-to-end, in the same way they placed the craft sticks, have them return to their seats and carefully cut out the paw print on student page 112.

THEN HAVE THE CHILDREN lay the paw prints end-to-end along Bear's path. *How many paw prints have you used so far? How many paw prints will there be after [child's name] puts one down?*

When the last paw print has been placed, gather the children to talk about what they did and to count the total number of paw prints. Examine the path together. *Are all the paw prints placed end-to-end? Are there some empty spaces or gaps between paw prints? Why is it important to line up the paw prints end-to-end?* When everyone agrees on the method and the result, record the measurement where everyone can see it.

Next, explain that you have made several other paths to measure. The children might enjoy pretending that these are Bear's paths to other destinations. Ask them to suggest some places Bear might go and label the ends of the paths accordingly.

HAVE CHILDREN WORK IN PAIRS or in small groups, using the paw prints (or another unit) to measure the paths. As you circulate among the groups, note how the children line up and count the units. Some paths may not be an exact number of units. If this happens, talk about the path as being a little more (or less) than _____ units long.

Bring the groups together to share their results. It will be helpful to do this in the area where the paths are. *How many craft sticks long was your group's path? How did you line up the craft sticks? Why? Which path is the longest? The shortest? How did you figure that out? How does lining up the craft sticks help you to find out?*

Explain that children will do some more measuring at home. Introduce student page 113. Point out the objects mentioned in items 1 and 2 and the units (paper strips) on the rest of the page. The children should cut out the strips, find the objects in their homes, use the strips to measure the length of each object, and record the lengths on student page 113. For the third item, children use the paper strips to measure the length of an object they choose.

## f.y.i.

--------------------------------------

You may wish to continue this lesson on the following day. If so, to close this portion of the lesson, have children draw a story about the problem, how they solved it, and what they found out.

## Student Pages

Student page 112 has a paw print for children to cut out and use as a non-standard unit of measure in class. Student page 113 asks children to cut out paper strips, use the strips to measure objects at home, and record the measurements.

## Assessment

As you observed children using nonstandard units to measure length, you could see how they chose units and then how they used them to measure. In particular, you could see if they lined up the units from the starting point to the end point and if they placed the units end-to-end without gaps or overlaps. You could also assess their ability to count the units accurately. In discussions, you noted how children described their methods and their reasons for using those methods. You also observed children comparing lengths that were expressed in the same units.

## NCTM Standards Summary

In this lesson, children built on their informal knowledge of length as they used nonstandard units to measure length. They developed both their understanding of measurement and their skill at manipulating units of measure through hands-on activities. They used problem solving as they improved their measuring methods and as they applied the methods to problem situations. They used communication as they discussed their methods of measuring and as they shared and recorded results.

**Answers**

*Page 112*
No answers required.

*Page 113*
1–3. Answers will vary.

# Exploring Length

**Cut out Bear's paw print.**
**Use the paw print to measure Bear's path.**

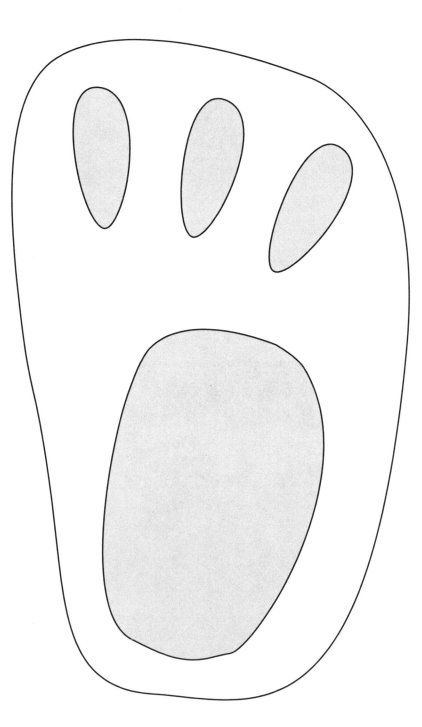

**Standard 4** Measurement

# Exploring Length

**Cut out the paper strips. Use the paper strips to measure each item.**

**1** Find an envelope. The envelope is _____ strips long.

**2** Find a table. The table is _____ strips long.

**3** Choose something to measure. The object is _____ strips long.

# Comparing Lengths

## Introduction

**Objective** → Children will compare objects to determine if they are longer, taller, shorter, tallest, shortest, or about the same length.

**Context** → This lesson is the beginning of a unit on measurement. In future lessons, children will be involved in comparing weight.

Name _____

**Comparing Lengths**

**1.** Color the longer pencil red and the shorter pencil blue.

**2.** Draw a rectangle about the same length as the longer train.

**3.** Draw a rectangle about the same length as the shorter train.

## NCTM Process Standards Analysis and Focus

The standards analysis examines how the process standards have been incorporated into the above lesson. By increasing the focus on three of the process standards, a more effective and meaningful lesson can be presented. The suggestions offered can help you to think about how this might be accomplished.

**Reasoning and Proof** The lesson has children compare objects and explain which are longer or shorter; however, children are asked to consider only adjacent objects.

*Suggestion* → Include comparisons of objects that are not placed directly next to one another. Plan activities that encourage children to make judgments about the relative heights and lengths

Name _____

Draw a tall cereal box showing your favorite cereal. Draw a
shorter cereal box showing your least favorite cereal.

of objects and then to check their
opinions by measuring.

**Communication** Teacher notes
suggest children explain their thinking
as they work with connecting cubes.

*Suggestion* → Discuss subtle
distinctions as children explore and
explain their comparisons. Such
discussions will help to clarify childrens'
thinking as well as offer a context in
which to use the vocabulary associated

with measurement such as *longer*,
*shortest*, and *same as*.

**Representation** Sound activities are
suggested in which children use
connecting cubes to represent a basis
against which to make comparisons
about length and height.

*Suggestion* → Have children compare
the lengths of dissimilar objects. This
will help draw attention to the idea that
when measuring length or height, a

linear measurement from a common
starting point is what needs to be
considered. Use nonstandard units to
help children discover the importance
and purpose of standard units.

**Problem Solving** Children are
asked to make comparisons, but
problem solving is not involved.

**Connections** Teacher notes
suggest making connections with
daily calendar routines by asking
children to identify longer and
shorter months.

The teaching plan that follows shows how the suggestions for increasing the focus on the process standards can be implemented.

## Revised Teaching Plan

**Materials** → Connecting cubes; a variety of objects of different sizes and shapes; paper clips; string; drawing paper; pencils; crayons; markers; butcher paper; sorting mats; recording sheets

INTRODUCE THE LESSON WITH A WHOLE-CLASS ACTIVITY. Have two volunteers of different heights stand in front of the class. Ask questions that encourage children to look carefully at the two children to compare their heights. *Who is taller? How could we describe the other person?* Ask another volunteer to join the group. *Of the three, who is the tallest? Who is the shortest?* Repeat the activity with another set of volunteers.

Expand the activity by having children make comparisons between one of the volunteers and a classroom object. *Is* [child's name] *taller or shorter than the bookcase? How can we check?* Allow time to try out suggested strategies. Compare another classmate with an object to reinforce understanding. Encourage children to include details to support the rationale behind their observations.

NEXT, DRAW CHILDREN'S ATTENTION to objects that are not standing on the same level. *Which would be taller, this book or the fish tank? How can we know for sure?* Use this type of comparison to demonstrate the idea that being taller or shorter is measured from a starting point in a vertical direction. Model how to compare the objects at the same starting point by moving the book next to the fish tank. Moving objects so that they are next to each other and aligning them at their base makes it easier to determine which is longer/longest, taller/tallest, or shorter/shortest. If time permits, choose two stationary objects to compare. Have children conjecture, then check, which of the two objects is shorter or taller. Brainstorm ways that children can check their conjectures. Possibilities might include using their arms or pieces of paper or string to measure objects. While children are not ready to use rulers or measuring tapes, activities like these create an awareness of the need for a measuring tool. Use these types of activities and questions ongoing throughout the school year to refine childrens' estimating skills and reinforce their understanding of height and length.

ORGANIZE SMALL-GROUP LEARNING ACTIVITIES to further develop childrens' understanding of the concepts of length and height. Select from activities below to explore the concepts in a variety of contexts. Rotate the activities throughout your day or week according to your schedule.

**Activity 1** Place a large assortment of objects—including long, thin ones and short, fat ones—into a large box. Make sure that some of the objects are about the same length. Also, create sorting mats with these labels: "shorter," "same length," "longer." Have a child select one object and place it on the mat of his or her choice. Have a second child select a second object, compare it to the first object, and place it on its respective mat. Continue calling on pairs of volunteers to choose and sort objects. Listen and observe as children sort. Ask them to share their thinking to help reinforce the concepts of same length, shorter, and longer.

**Activity 2** Work with a small group of children around a table. Place a large container of connecting cubes in the middle of the table. Create three towers with the cubes, making sure that one is shorter than the other two. Ask children to describe the towers, especially noting how the towers are different. In your discussion, use vocabulary such as *shorter*, *taller*, and *same*. Next, remove two of the towers and focus attention on the remaining one. Ask a volunteer to make a tower that is taller, shorter, or the same height as the remaining tower and have the group compare the two.

You may wish to expand the activity by having children create connecting-cube trains in order to explore the concept of longer/longest. Use your discussion to demonstrate how length is generally a horizontal measure, while height is a vertical measure. Explain that when the connecting cubes are placed flat on the table, we talk about their length. When the cubes are standing up, we talk about their height.

**f.y.i.**

------------------------------------

When using objects such as pencils or markers for comparison activities, be sure to vary them by including different thicknesses and lengths. Completely dissimilar objects should also be used for comparisons. It is important for children to understand that an object's shape or form is not an important consideration when measuring length or height.

**Activity 3** Place crayons, markers, and paper at a center. Ask children to draw pictures of similar objects that are different heights to illustrate a comparison. Have children dictate descriptions of their pictures, such as "The striped jump rope is longer than the blue jump rope."

**Activity 4** Cut large sheets of butcher paper into 3-foot sections. Have an adult volunteer trace children's outlines onto the paper. After children decorate their outlines, cut them out and place them around the room in groups of two or three. Be sure to align the figures' feet so that "children" are standing on the same level. Then work with children to make comparisons. Record their observations about height, such as "Mary is shorter than Charlie." "Tom is taller than Charlie." Display children's observations next to the sets of figures. Learning experiences such as these help children look for specific characteristics and clarify their thinking.

**Activity 5** Have pairs of children find and compare objects in the classroom to a specific length such as a connecting-cube train, paper-clip chain, or length of string. In advance, prepare a recording sheet similar to the one shown on the following page. First, instruct partners to find three classroom objects that might be longer, shorter, or the same length as the connecting cubes, paper clips, or string. Then, have children draw a picture on their recording sheets to represent each of the objects chosen. Next, have children use the connecting cubes, paper clips, or string to measure the actual length of each object and record it on the sheet next to its picture. Plan time for partners to share their findings. Hands-on experiences such as these help children to internalize concepts of measurement.

Incorporate activities and games throughout the day that encourage children to think about the concepts of height and length.

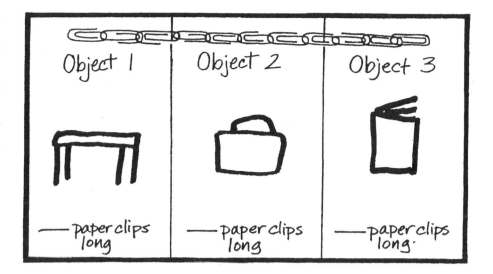

## Student Pages

Children are now ready to complete exercises similar to those on the reduced student pages.

## Assessment

Observing children's actions and listening to their responses provided information about their level of understanding. By observing how children sorted objects, it was possible to assess their understanding of the concepts of shorter, longer, and the same length. There were also opportunities to determine if children understood how to compare objects as they compared their connecting-cube train, paper-clip train, or length of string to objects around the classroom to check their conjectures.

## NCTM Standards Summary

A broad range of learning activities allowed basic concepts of measurement to be developed in meaningful contexts. Inviting children to speculate about the comparative lengths and heights of objects provided an excellent vehicle for promoting reasoning, communication, and problem-solving experiences. Children selected objects to compare, they made determinations about the relative heights and lengths of objects, and then found ways to check their thinking using informal measuring techniques. Encouraging children to explain their findings and use appropriate terms as they explained their thinking helped to reinforce their understanding of the concepts being developed.

# Standard 5 Data Analysis and Probability

AT THE KINDERGARTEN LEVEL, data analysis and probability includes a lot of work with sorting groups of objects, different graphical representations, and probability concepts. Our lessons are derived from these important topics, and include a lesson on sorting a group of objects by different attributes, a lesson in which children create bar graphs, a lesson that has children identify possible and impossible outcomes, and a lesson on sorting a group of objects by a single attribute.

Three lessons model how the process standards can be used to teach content. A fourth lesson is a hypothetical textbook lesson that we have revised to be more standards based. These four lessons do not represent the entire curriculum, but rather provide glimpses of how, with a more concentrated effort to incorporate the process standards, better mathematics teaching and learning can be achieved.

In one lesson we have chosen, children sort a collection of objects by different attributes. By incorporating the process standards of problem solving, representation, and communication into this lesson, children actually sort through objects themselves, rather than just being given graphs to examine.

Another lesson we have chosen is one that focuses on creating a bar graph. In this lesson, children sort objects by color, then make a bar graph showing the number of objects for each color. Through the process standards of representation and communication, children combine the two ways to represent data, sorting and graphing, in one lesson. Children decide which is the better way for a particular situation.

A third lesson we have chosen is one in which children recognize possible and impossible outcomes. Children examine many representations of probability experiments. They use communication and reasoning and proof to decide if an outcome is possible or if it is not possible.

The hypothetical textbook lesson we have chosen to revise is one that has children sort a group of objects by a single attribute. Through better incorporation of the process standards of communication, reasoning and proof, and connections, children discuss sorting and when and how they sort in their everyday experiences. Children then try to find objects in the classroom that share a common attribute with an object that they have previously chosen.

## Standard 5 Lessons

Sorting by Different Attributes

Creating Bar Graphs

Recognizing Possible and Impossible Outcomes

Sorting by a Single Attribute

# Sorting by Different Attributes

## Introduction

----------------------------------------

**Objective** → Children will describe and sort a collection of objects by different attributes and will discuss the sorted data.

**Context** → Children have counted and can show cardinality. In future lessons, they will continue representing objects in tables and graphs.

## NCTM Standards Focus

In this lesson, children decide how to display and record data using an assortment of lids. When children physically handle objects, they are better able to describe their attributes than if they had to determine attributes from illustrations on a page. The physical act of sorting helps children to understand better the need for graphing and to understand graphs. Often, children are given graphs to examine without the experience of physically sorting the objects. This standards-based lesson provides children with these experiences.

**Problem Solving** Children use attributes of the objects they sort to find different ways to group them. They move from the most obvious attributes to less obvious ones. They find ways to compare groups to see if there are more, fewer, or equal numbers of objects in the different groups.

**Representation** Children represent the way they sorted the objects by drawing pictures of the groups they sorted and by showing the number in each group.

**Communication** Children describe the different groups they sorted objects into. They communicate the attributes that distinguished one group from the others and tell how they can compare the groups.

## Teaching Plan

**Materials** → Student pages 126–127; a container filled with an assortment of lids or tops, such as lids from milk or juice cartons, tops from detergents, shampoo, or other cleaning products, metal or plastic lids from jars of food; large poster board; chart paper; small plastic or paper bags; construction paper for use as a work mat

**G**ATHER CHILDREN IN A LARGE open area in the classroom. Place the poster board in the center of the space, and spill the lids onto it. Be sure that all children can see the lids.

Have children carefully inspect the assortment of lids and tops on the floor and think about how they would describe them. Record children's descriptions on chart paper. Here are some attributes children should note:

| | | |
|---|---|---|
| tall | different colors | round |
| short | smooth | fat |
| flat | rough | skinny |

GIVE EACH CHILD a lid, and have them describe the lid to a partner using as many different attributes as possible. Listen to the words children use in their descriptions. Then have children share the terms they used with the class. The more terms children are familiar with, the easier it will be for them to figure out different ways to sort.

*If we were to put all the lids together again, how could we then sort them into groups?* Encourage partners to come up with some ways, and then have children share with the class some of the different ways to sort the lids. Have the class decide on the way they want to sort the lids.

**f.y.i.**

------------------------------------

You will need lids for the opening whole class activity. You will also need lids for an activity midway through the lesson when each pair of children will need a bag of lids. Make sure that each bag has several lids with like and different attributes. If you want to keep these bags for several lessons, use self-closing plastic bags. Send a note home asking children to bring different kinds of lids to school.

---

### What Might Happen . . . What to Do

------------------------------------------------------------

This might be the first time some children have had an opportunity to sort objects by attributes other than color, size, and shape. As they are working as a whole group, encourage these children to look for other details on the lids. These details might be ridges on the lids or writing on the lids. *What kinds of things do you notice on the outside of the lids that could help you to sort them in different ways? If you sorted the lids by the ones with writing and the ones without writing, how many groups would you have? Can you have a group with only one lid?*

---

Show children where to place each group on the poster board, and have children place their lids according to the way the class decided to sort them. *What can you tell us about these groups?* If this open-ended question is too vague, ask more specific questions. *Which of these groups has the most lids? Do any of these groups have the same number of lids?* You may wish to have children match the lids one-to-one when comparing the number of lids in the different groups.

Encourage children to discuss the specific strategies they used when determining the number of lids in each group. *How did you know if one group had more lids than another group?* Children should respond to questions about "how many" by counting. *How would you count these lids?* Observe how children count.

GIVE EACH PAIR OF CHILDREN a bag with lids in a variety of sizes and a sheet of construction paper to use as a work mat. Allow time for partners to explore their lids and describe them to one another.

---

### What Might Happen . . . What to Do

- - - - - - - - - - - - - - - - - - - - - - - - - - - - - - - - - - - - - - - - - - - - - - - - - - - - -

If this is the first time children are using lids, it is likely that they will need more time than you have available in the lesson to explore them. Prior to this lesson, place the lids in a center where children can use them to stack, make patterns, or trace around them.

---

Have each pair of children decide how to sort their lids. As children are sorting the lids, circulate among them. *What attribute did you use to sort your lids? Which group has the most lids? What did you do to find out if that group had the most lids? If I was going to write a label for this group, what would the label say?*

Distribute several copies of student page 126 to each pair. Have children draw each group on a separate sheet and show how many lids there are in each one. If they know how to write, have them write the attribute for each group. If they do not know how to write, ask them to dictate the attributes for the different groups so that you may write them. Discuss the different ways the children sorted the lids. Focus on the different attributes they used. If there's time, have them sort their lids a different way.

## Student Pages

Most of student page 126 has been left for children to draw their groups and record their sorting attributes. If they know how to write, children can write their responses. If they do not know how to write, have them use the back of the page to draw different ways to sort. Student page 127 presents buttons that have been sorted according to the number of buttonholes. Encourage children to color the buttons not according to the groups they are in, but to look for different attributes. You might want to have children do this page at home.

## Assessment

Throughout the lesson, there were opportunities to assess whether children understood how to isolate specific variables in order to place lids in like groups. In addition, you could assess children's language skills and attention to detail. You observed children's ability to count and use cardinality as they discussed and compared data.

## NCTM Standards Summary

Children used problem-solving strategies as they grappled with different ideas about sorting the lids. They listened to attributes their classmates communicated to find more ways to sort. They represented the attributes by sorting and by drawing the groups. They communicated their understanding of the different attributes by describing how the lids fit into the groups in which they placed them. Children used their understanding of quantity by counting and comparing the groups.

**Answers**

*Page 126*
Answers will vary.

*Page 127*
1. the buttons with 4 buttonholes
2. 6 buttons
3. Answers will vary.
4. Answers will vary.

## Sorting by Different Attributes

**Draw groups to show how you sorted the lids.**

❶ Tell how you sorted.

_____

_____

_____

❷ How many are in each group?

_____

# Sorting by Different Attributes

**Tell how the buttons are sorted.**

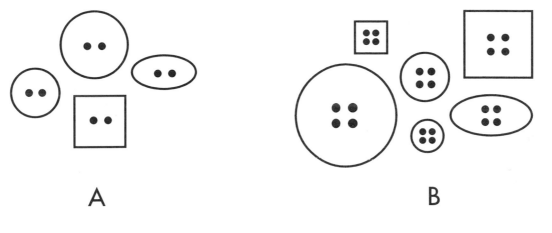

A                                           B

**1** Which group has the most buttons? _____

**2** How many are there? _____

**3** Color the buttons.

**4** How can you sort the buttons another way?

_____

_____

_____

# Creating Bar Graphs

## Introduction

------------------------------------

**Objective** → Children will represent and interpret data using concrete objects, sort the objects by color, and represent the data on a bar graph.

**Context** → Children have sorted, counted, and compared objects. They have made real graphs and pictographs. This is the first lesson on bar graphs.

## NCTM Standards Focus

In this lesson, children will display, represent, and record data in two ways. They will determine when sorting is all they need to do and when graphing provides them with the information they need. This standards-based lesson combines two ways of organizing information: sorting and graphing.

**Representation** Children use charts and connecting cubes to show different methods of representing information.

**Connections** Children make connections between the information they have gathered and the representations of the information. They also make connections between the different representations.

**Communication** Children learn a new way of communicating information. They review previous methods of communicating information through the use of graphs. During the lesson children communicate different strategies and ideas to their classmates.

## Teaching Plan

**Materials** → Student pages 132–133

**Preparation** → Prepare the following materials for each pair of children. Make an additional set of materials for demonstration purposes.

— a bag of 25 cubes (containing cubes of as many as 5 different colors, but no more that 8 cubes of one color) with some kind of identifying mark such as *Bag A* on the bag (Bags need not be identical for each group.)

— crayons or markers of the same colors as the connecting cubes

— an 8 × 11 sheet of construction paper for pairs to use as a work mat

BEGIN THE LESSON by telling children that you have several bags of cubes and that you are going to give a bag to each pair of children. Explain that you need to find out how many cubes of each color are in each bag. Tell them you also need a record of what each bag contains so that you don't have to look in the bags to find out.

Show the children your bag. *What can we do to find out how many cubes of each color are in each bag?* (Empty the bag and sort the cubes.) Empty the bag and have children tell how many cubes there are of each color. *How can we make a record of the number of cubes of each color?*

## What Children Might Say

- Write the number for each color.
- Make a chart.
- Draw a picture of the cubes and color them.
- Connect cubes of one color together and write how many there are.

Tell children that now we need to make a record and the first one that they will make is a chart. Discuss with them charts that may already be in the room, such as a job chart, and how they may wish to make their chart. One simple way would be to make a patch of each color and write the number of cubes next to it. Also make sure to talk to children about a title and why it is important to put a title on the chart. Children should understand that people do not just make charts to make them, but rather to communicate information.

Now tell children they are going to make a different type of representation, a real graph. Take a minute to discuss the graphs they have made before. On your own chart, show children how they can arrange the cubes to make a real graph. Discuss with children whether or not they want to connect the cubes for their real graphs. They can make it whichever way they want, it will still be a real graph. Later, when they make the bar graph, they will see that it is an extension of the cubes being connected.

When children are done with their real graphs, discuss what they did. Talk about what they liked about showing the information this way. Also, discuss what some of the problems were. Now tell them they are going to record the information in a new way, a bar graph.

Take student page 132 and place it by your demonstration real graph. Show children the grid. Ask them how they might use the real graph to make a graph showing how many cubes there are. Make sure that during the discussion children understand that the left side shows the number of cubes.

Now make the demonstration graph with children helping. Make sure to make identifiers at the bottom of each bar. Use the actual colors and the names for each color. Coloring the bars the actual colors may also help children identify the bars.

Make sure the graph has a title. Talk about how the bar graph and the real graph are similar and different. An important point for children to see in the bar graph is that they do not have to count the individual units like in the real graph. They can look at the top of the bar and tell how many cubes there are instead of having to count.

Before children go back to their desks, review the parts of the graph. Have children make the graph. Circulate as they work and leave the graph you made in a convenient place. Make sure children understand that their bags probably have different numbers of cubes, and while their graphs are similar, they will not look alike.

---

### What Might Happen . . . What to Do

Children might have trouble coloring the correct number of cubes. You may want to have them put the actual bar right next to where they are coloring. Also they could put the bar next to the space and make a line at the top and color down.

## Student Pages

Student pages 132 and 133 provide grids for children to use to make bar graphs. Page 132 is for use with two-centimeter cubes and page 133 is for use with three-quarter inch cubes.

## Assessment

As children were working with the connecting cubes, you assessed their knowledge of sorting and numbering. Children also showed their knowledge of comparison strategies and comparison terminology. The graph allowed you another means of evaluating children's knowledge of comparison between quantities as well as terminology.

## NCTM Standards Summary

Children looked at different methods of communicating information and the benefits of each in attempting to solve a problem. They then actually made the different representations to communicate the information. They connected the three types of representation and communication.

**Answers**

*Page 132*
Graphs will vary

*Page 133*
Graphs will vary.

# Creating Bar Graphs

**Use this page to make your graph.**

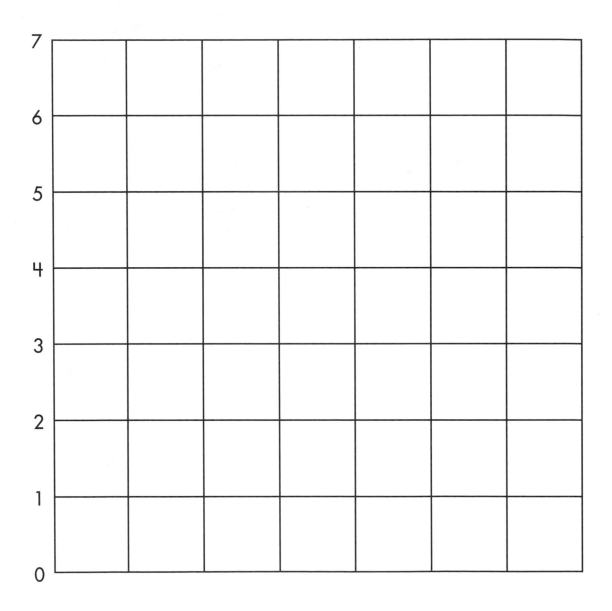

# Creating Bar Graphs

**Use this page to make your graph.**

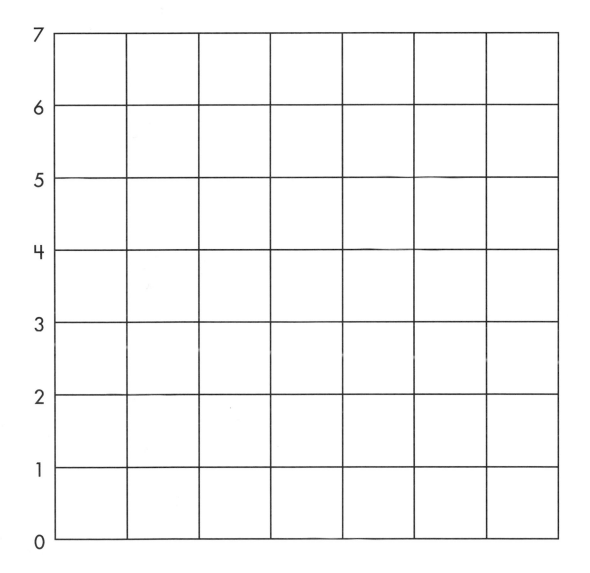

# Recognizing Possible and Impossible Outcomes

## Introduction

------------------------------------

**Objective** → Children will recognize possible and impossible outcomes in a given situation.

**Context** → Children have used number cubes and recognize numerals 1 through 6. They will use the notion of possible and impossible outcomes in mathematical and everyday situations.

## NCTM Standards Focus

Often children are asked to determine possible/impossible events just from illustrations. This has its drawbacks because of children's vivid imaginations. In this standards-based lesson, children are given several concrete situations. They use a number cube, a two-color counter, and decide what is possible and what is impossible. They use two methods—conducting an experiment and finding all the possible outcomes—to determine whether something is impossible or possible.

**Reasoning and Proof** Children make and investigate mathematical conjectures. They reason whether or not given situations are possible. They show that situations are impossible if they cannot occur.

**Representation** Children represent possible outcomes of a two-color counter, a bag with cubes, and a number cube using different recording methods and conclude that certain events are impossible with the help of these representations.

**Communication** Children communicate their understanding of when situations are possible and why a situation is impossible. They share their conclusions with the rest of the class.

## Teaching Plan

**Materials** → Student pages 138–139; paper for recording information from the experiments (one sheet for each group for each experiment); a number cube labeled with numbers 1–6; one two-color counter; one set of three different colored cubes and an opaque bag

**T**HIS LESSON CAN EITHER be done as a whole class or in small groups. It will probably be better to do at least the first activity together to help children understand what they are doing. Also, three experiments are suggested here. Depending on the time you have you may wish to focus on one or two experiments and save another for later.

Ask the children if they can tell you what it means if something is possible. Have them give examples of things they believe might be possible. Then ask them what it means if something is impossible. Again, have them give examples of something that is impossible. Make sure children give their reasons as to why they think something is either possible or impossible. Have them try to convince other children that whatever they are saying is impossible or possible. If disagreements arise about whether something is possible or impossible, focus on what the class could do to find out which it is. This will help set the stage for what will happen later in the lesson. Also, it will work on developing their ability to reason.

Now bring out your bag with three cubes (for example red, blue, and white). Make sure children have paper to record the color of the cubes as they are drawn out of the bag. Show the children the cubes that are in the bag. Tell them you are going to pick out a cube and then put it back. When you pick out the cube, they should record the color. *What cubes is it possible for me to pick out? Do you think that a green cube could come out of the bag?* You may want to ask for a thumbs up or thumbs down vote for whether different outcomes are possible. This way you can see what each child thinks.

Discuss different ways that they can record the results. Some may wish to put the color on their paper and tally, and some may want to make a tally mark of the color of the cube. Ask them to get what they need ready. Tell them to make a spot for green and to get their green crayon out just in case they need to use it.

Now conduct the experiment. Draw one cube and have children record the results. Repeat this ten times. Discuss the results in terms of what they said earlier was possible and impossible. Review again why they thought some were possible or impossible. Take out all the cubes and line them up so children can easily see all the possible outcomes. Discuss with children how knowing all the possible outcomes can can be used as a method to see if something is possible or impossible.

**f.y.i.**

--------------------------------------

Children are using two different techniques to check on the possibility and impossibility of certain outcomes. One method is to check for all possible outcomes. In the example with the cubes and the bags, checking the colors of all the cubes is finding all the outcomes. The other method is running an experiment. The experiment method is not totally valid for showing that a green cube will not come up. However, since a green cube did not come up, children can see that the experiment did not show green was possible. The experiment helped support their belief that green was impossible. Having children see that the event is not in the data set will tell them whether or not it is possible or impossible.

Show children a two-color counter (for example yellow and red) and give them a new piece of paper for the experiment. Tell them that you will flip the counter and they will record what happens. Ask them what they think the possible outcomes are and why they think that. Ask them if they think that blue could come up after you flipped the counter. Discuss why they believe this.

Discuss with children how they would like to record this experiment. Make sure they have a way to record blue if it should come up. Repeat the experiment ten times. Ask the children if they think that if you flipped the counter more times it would come up blue at least once, and why. Discuss the outcome of the experiment again, focusing on what was possible and what was impossible. Check with children to see if the results agreed with what they thought.

For the final experiment, bring out the number cube and show it to the children. Give them another piece of recording paper. Have a similar discussion with children about what is possible and impossible, and why. Use the number zero as a suggestion for the impossible number. Also have them set up their recording systems. You may need to do this experiment a few more times than the others since there are more possible outcomes. Discuss the results when the experiment is done.

---

### What Might Happen . . . What to Do

The cube might present a problem to some children in determining the data set since they may get confused as to what numbers they have seen and not seen. One method that may help them is to put a small piece of masking tape on the number once they have written it down.

---

To end the lesson, ask children to discuss ways they can tell whether something is possible or not. It may help to give them some concrete examples similar to the examples used in class. Help them focus on using the technique of finding all the possible outcomes.

## Student Pages

Student page 138 asks children to represent something that is possible. Student page 139 asks children to represent something that is impossible.

## Assessment

During this lesson, you had several opportunities to assess children's understanding of the terms *possible* and *impossible*. You were able to see individual children's responses for each experiment. Also at the end of the lesson you were able to look at their response for individual examples.

## NCTM Standards Summary

Children used reasoning in concrete situations to determine whether outcomes were possible or impossible. They represented possible outcomes by recording information in experiments investigating the situation. They communicated their understanding of when situations are possible and shared their understanding about why a situation is impossible.

**Answers**

*Page 138*
Answers will vary.

*Page 139*
Answers will vary.

# Recognizing Possible and Impossible Outcomes

**Draw a picture of something that would be possible.**

# Recognizing Possible and Impossible Outcomes

## Draw a picture of something that would be impossible.

# Sorting by a Single Attribute

## Introduction

------------------------------------

**Objective** → Children will sort objects into groups based on a single attribute.

**Context** → Children have discussed the concept of length and have used nonstandard units such as paper clips to measure length. Future experiences may include sorting objects into groups based on more than one attribute.

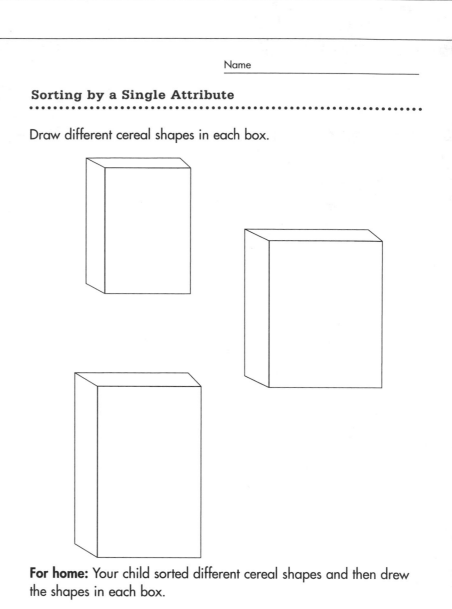

Name _____

**Sorting by a Single Attribute**
••••••••••••••••••••••••••••••••••••••••••••••••••••••

Draw different cereal shapes in each box.

**For home:** Your child sorted different cereal shapes and then drew the shapes in each box.

## NCTM Process Standards Analysis and Focus

The standards analysis examines how the process standards have been incorporated into the above lesson. By increasing the focus on three of the process standards, a more effective and meaningful lesson can be presented. The suggestions offered can help you to think about how this might be accomplished.

**Communication** Suggestions in the teachers' notes include activities that promote discussions about how objects are alike and different. Children are also asked to talk about how they sorted various objects.

*Suggestion* → **Take time to discuss what sorting means. Brainstorm different ways to sort a given collection of objects. Utilize real-world experiences to discuss the reasons why familiar**

Name _____

............................................................

Draw different colored counters in each ring.

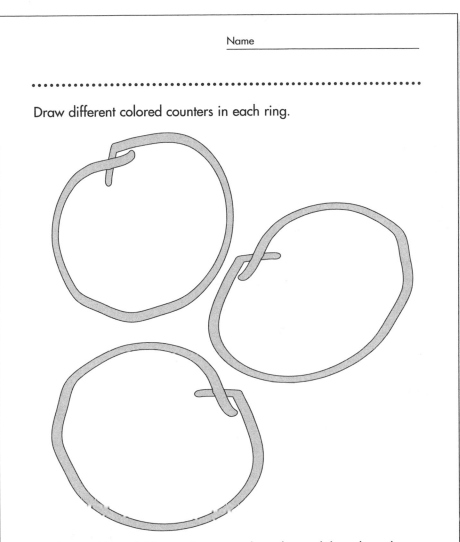

**For home:** Your child sorted counters by color and then drew the counters in the spaces.

objects at home or in the classroom are sorted in particular ways. Encourage children to use appropriate terminology such as size, color, and shape as they describe attributes.

**Reasoning and Proof** Children are asked to compare given objects and to describe their similarities or differences.

*Suggestion* → Plan activities that involve children in identifying and

sorting groups of objects by attributes they have in common. Ask children to choose an item in the classroom, select one of its attributes such as color, shape, or size to focus on, and then find other objects in the classroom that can be grouped with their item based on the chosen attribute. This type of activity challenges children's ability to think critically as they bring together a diverse collection of objects.

**Connections** Activities involve children in identifying physical attributes of various objects and then making connections between the objects based on a similar attribute.

*Suggestion* → Consider a variety of ways to help children see relationships between objects that are grouped together and the attributes of those groupings. Discuss familiar situations both at home and at school that require sorting. Challenge children to describe possible rationales for each situation. These types of experiences help children to look for and internalize common-alities among objects.

**Problem Solving** Although the ability to sort objects requires thoughtful consideration, problem solving is not part of this lesson.

**Representation** Cereals of various shapes and counters of different colors are suggested as sorting materials.

The teaching plan that follows shows how the suggestions for increasing the focus on the process standards can be implemented.

## Revised Teaching Plan

**Materials** → Construction paper in a variety of colors; attribute cards; an assortment of objects that can be sorted by shape, color, use, and size; chart paper; an assortment of magazine pictures; markers

**B**EGIN THE LESSON BY HOLDING UP a sheet of construction paper. Ask children who are wearing the color displayed to sit together in a circle. Repeat with other colors until all children are seated in the circle. Explain that children came to the circle in groups based on something they had in common. Point out that in this instance color was the common factor. Explain that very often things are grouped together because they have something in common.

Ask children to look around the classroom for objects that are grouped together because they are alike in some way. Have a volunteer identify one such set of objects, such as wooden blocks, books on a shelf, bins of crayons, paints, and so on. If possible, bring the set of objects to the front of the room. Encourage children to look carefully at the objects. Have volunteers tell ways the objects are alike as well as ways they are different. Challenge children to determine the basis of the grouping. In your discussion, use words that describe attributes, such as size, color, shape, type of material, or function. *How are these objects grouped? Why do you suppose they are grouped this way?* Help children to understand that grouping objects by a similar attribute makes the objects easier to locate and manage.

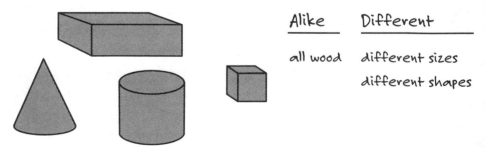

| Alike | Different |
|---|---|
| all wood | different sizes |
| | different shapes |

Explain to children that when we group objects together by something they have in common, we are *sorting* those things. Initiate a discussion about familiar objects at home or at school that children have seen sorted. List children's ideas on chart paper. *Have you ever helped put groceries away after shopping? Describe what you did and tell why. Think about your clothes at home. Are they all mixed up in a drawer? How are they arranged? Why? Can you think of other situations that call for sorting?* Discuss a broad range of ideas such as sorting clothes for laundry, putting away dishes and silverware, and organizing toys and sports equipment. Using familiar situations and objects helps children to see the usefulness of sorting.

PLACE A VARIETY OF OBJECTS that can be grouped together by a single attribute in the center of the circle. Consider objects such as a red crayon, a red block, a yellow pencil, a yellow car, a piece of chalk, a green truck, a green block, and so on. Ask children to look at the objects and discuss how the objects are alike and different. *How can we sort these items?* Children might make suggestions such as putting the car with the truck because they both can be driven, the crayon with the chalk and pencil because they can be used to write, or putting the red objects together. Decide on one suggestion and have a volunteer group the items together based on the suggestion. Take time to discuss the items grouped together. *How are these items alike? How are they different?* Encourage children to describe items by the attribute they have in common to reinforce the basis of the grouping. Then place all of the items together again. *Is there another way to sort these things?* Repeat the activity several times to sort the items in different ways.

| red crayon | yellow pencil | yellow car | chalk | green truck | green block |

ORGANIZE SMALL-GROUP LEARNING ACTIVITIES to further develop children's understandings of how to sort objects based on a single attribute. Select activities below to explore the concept in a variety of contexts. Rotate the activities according to your schedule.

**Activity 1** Name two or three objects such as bus, plane, and bicycle. Have children raise a hand if they can name something the three objects have in common. Vary the activity by having children name one way the objects are different. Continue with other objects. Possible groupings might include:

> a basketball, a football, a golf ball
>
> sweater, hat, coat
>
> soup, ice cream, stew
>
> bus, plane, bicycle
>
> cat, dog, lion

**Activity 2** Place a piece of paper, glue, and a variety of magazine pages with familiar images such as different types of pets, snacks, or people, on a tray in the learning center. Have pairs of children select images from the magazine pages based on a single attribute and glue the images onto the paper. Then have children dictate or write the attribute they considered when they sorted the images.

**Activity 3** Play 'What's the Same?' Form groups of two to four players and have players sit in a circle. Give each player a box with an assortment of attribute blocks. Instruct children that each player is to take one block from his/her box and place it in front of him/her. One player should then name an attribute the blocks have in common, either shape, color, size, or thickness. That player should identify all blocks that have the attribute named, take the common blocks, and stack them. The remaining blocks should be returned to their respective boxes. Players take turns identifying common attributes and stacking until all blocks have been removed from the boxes.

**Activity 4** Place a variety of objects into a plastic tub. Have children take turns deciding different ways to sort the objects. Provide paper and markers for children to illustrate one way to sort the objects and their grouping choice. Allow time for children to describe the different ways they sorted the objects. Encourage children to use words such as *sort*, *group*, *large*, *small*, *alike*, and *different* as well as color names and shape names.

These types of learning activities help children to make connections and see relationships between objects. They also provide an opportunity for children to use the language of mathematics in a meaningful context.

CONCLUDE THE LESSON with an invitation to children to build their own collections of objects. Work with children to determine a single attribute each will use to build his/her collection. Briefly highlight different attributes such as color, shape, or size to be considered as a criterion for grouping. Provide trays for children to display their objects. After children have assembled their collections, allow time for sharing. As each child displays a collection, encourage others to determine the sorting criterion.

## Student Pages

Children should now be ready to complete exercises similar to those on the reduced student pages. Take time to listen to children describe their completed pages.

## Assessment

As children sorted both concrete objects and pictures by a single attribute, it was possible to assess the level of their understanding. Their ability to identify and sort objects by a single attribute could also be assessed as they made and discussed their sorting collections.

## NCTM Standards Summary

A broad range of language-rich experiences helped to reinforce children's knowledge about sorting objects based on a single attribute. Discussing the rationale for sorting strengthened their understanding of this concept. Children were asked to think critically about attributes and to identify similarities between objects that would constitute a basis for sorting them into groups. Supporting their decisions with specific details as they made connections between items for grouping purposes helped develop classification skills and logic, both of which are essential when classifying abstract data. Making connections to familiar real-world situations and objects helped children to internalize relationships and develop confidence in their ability to identify attributes and carry out sorting activities.

# Create Your Own Lesson

**T**HIS LAST CHAPTER IS DESIGNED TO HELP you develop your own lessons in which you can comfortably incorporate the NCTM standards with your teaching style. We start with a list of questions to help you focus on factors to consider as you begin to organize a standards-based lesson. Then we model the process used to create a lesson as you are walked through the thoughts and decisions one person used in developing a lesson.

The questions listed here are meant as a guide, a starting point; they are offered to get you thinking about how to develop your lesson, what material to cover, what steps to follow, what questions to ask. Hopefully, these questions will trigger additional ideas that you will add as you go along.

Write down the ideas that come to you as you read each question. There may be questions for which you don't have an immediate response, but don't worry; as you begin working on your lesson, ideas will come. Start by selecting the general content area. Think about the concept you want to develop. Then, narrow in on an objective for the lesson. Be specific and be realistic. What does meeting that objective mean? Is there a skill that students should be able to perform after completing the lesson? Are there questions they should be able to answer? How will you determine that the objective has been met?

Next, think about the process standards: Problem Solving, Reasoning and Proof, Communication, Connections, and Representation. What approach will be effective in helping students understand the concept? Try to envision how the lesson will flow, how it should begin, what activities and questions will be included, and how you will assess learning. Understand that there can be several ways to successfully teach any lesson. As you begin to design your lesson, new ideas will come and you will be able to refine your thinking.

# Focusing Questions

1. What content standard is to be addressed? What concept within that standard is to be developed?

2. What information do the standards offer about this content?

3. What do students know about this content? What don't they know?

4. What is the specific objective of the lesson? What should students be able to do at the end of the lesson?

   | | | |
   |---|---|---|
   | recognize | identify | define |
   | review | compute | classify |
   | compare | create | other |

5. What kinds of questions should students be able to answer when they complete this lesson? What skill(s) should they be able to demonstrate?

6. What resources are available to develop this concept?

   | | |
   |---|---|
   | references | textual material |
   | manipulatives | supplementary material |
   | colleagues | student knowledge |

7. What can realistically be accomplished in the time allowed?

8. Which activities and process standards can best help develop the key ideas?
   - using drawings, charts, diagrams (Representation)
   - focusing on symbols (Representation)
   - conducting small-group/large-group discussion (Communication)
   - having students gather and analyze data (Problem Solving)
   - thinking through relationships and explaining them (Reasoning and Proof and Communication)
   - finding ways to prove thinking and verify solutions (Reasoning and Proof)
   - extending/building on former knowledge (Connections)
   - integrating the concept with another discipline (Connections)
   - relating math to its use in the real world (Connections)

9. What questions will focus students' thinking on the concept and help guide learning?

## Developing the Lesson

I WANT TO DEVELOP A LESSON THAT addresses the ordinals for numbers one through five. This is part of Content Standard 1: Number and Operation. The standards suggest that children should understand numbers and relationships among numbers. So, before making sure children know the ordinal numbers, I want to make sure that my children understand the concept of ordinal numbers. Because the Standards emphasize that children should learn math in meaningful contexts, I need to think of a way that the children use order in their everyday lives, and then apply the ordinal numbers to it.

I know my children are already familiar with the concept of a correct order because so many things we do in kindergarten are routine and have a definite order to them. I just need to guide them to apply what they already know to the ordinals.

My children already know their numbers to twenty and are developing number sense with these numbers. I know my children are aware that order describes the relationship among numbers. They might say, "Three comes after two." Knowing the ordinals will help them affirm and understand the relationships among numbers and contribute to their number sense. My goal is for the children to understand the concept of order. My objective is for them to apply this concept by using the ordinal numbers first through fifth.

I will use an established classroom routine to help children understand ordinals. Communication needs to be an integral part of this lesson. Often when we use ordinals we use them to communicate to others. As the children tell me about the order of a routine, I'll write it down. Then we can apply the ordinals to the routine. The children can also illustrate their own order story. Playing *Simon Says* and using manipulatives will provide another way for them to represent ordinals, and a way for me to assess their thinking.

I've found that four of the process standards can help develop this lesson— Connections (classroom routine), Communication (children's narration), Representation (my recording of their narration, their story, manipulatives, and *Simon Says*), and Reasoning and Proof (how they apply the ordinals). I think these are the most important for this concept.

Now for the specifics of the lesson. I would like the lesson to begin with the children together as a group. Because the ordinals are totally new for the children, I will need to help the them make the connection between the cardinals and the ordinals. They will need to see, hear, and repeat the ordinals before they are able to work individually with some confidence. Working on their own will allow them to explore the ordinals independently. Coming back together as a group for *Simon Says* will help reinforce the ordinals for the players as well as for the observers.

As for materials, nothing special is required. The prior knowledge and experience the children have about their day will be a sufficient resource for the order story they are going to narrate. I will use chart paper, but I will have to prepare the paper the children are going to use. I should fold the paper into fifths. This will help the children delineate their morning into separate events and record them in a linear fashion as opposed to randomly on the paper.

## Problem 1

**For the routine, or "order story," I will ask the children to narrate the first five events in our morning. I will number the events and then use the cardinal numbers as a bridge to the ordinals.**

I will prepare for the order story by asking the children to think about what would happen at the beginning of a day at school if everybody does something out of order—this way the children can realize how order is important. *What happens to the beginning of our day if John waters the plants before going to his table.* Hopefully the children will realize that the beginning of our day would be one big mess. I will tell the children that we are going to write an order story. I will start by asking, *If we want to have a good day, what is the first thing we need to do when we come into the room?* I realize I am using an ordinal number in this question. I will be curious to see if the children use other ordinals, or words such as "next" and "then," as they begin to narrate the story. I need to make sure to write the five events in the center of the paper so I'll have room to write down the cardinals and ordinals below the corresponding event.

### Discussing Problem 1

This discussion is crucial because this is where I will introduce the children to the ordinals. I need to make sure that I set up the opportunity for the children to make the connection between the cardinals and the ordinals.

I will read the story back to them and ask the children to help me list the things we do. As they list them, I will write the cardinal number next to the item. The children know the cardinal numbers one through five, so this will help the children see the events in a linear order and provide a bridge for the ordinals when I write them down next.

1. **In the morning we hang up our coats.**
2. **We put our books in our cubbies.**
3. **We sit at the right table.**

I'll say, *When we count what we do in the morning we say one, two, three, four, five, but when we name things in an order we can say first, second, third, fourth, fifth.* I will read the story back to them like this: *In the morning the **first** thing we do is hang up our coats. The **second** thing we do is put our books and supplies in our cubbies.* I'll write the ordinals down next to the corresponding cardinal. Since many children are accustomed to counting with their fingers, I will also hold up my fingers as a representation of the numbers.

1. **first**    **In the morning we hang up our coats.**
2. **second**    **We put our books in our cubbies.**
3. **third**    **We sit at the right table.**

I will ask for volunteers to read the story, or list what we do in the morning, so the children can practice saying and using the ordinals. I will continue to emphasize that *when we count we say one, two, three, four, five, but when we name things in an order, we say first, second, third, fourth, fifth.*

## Problem 2

I will instruct the children to draw an individual story about the first five events in their morning before they come to school. To reinforce that I expect the children to put one event in each box, I will ask for a volunteer to state an event and point to the corresponding section on his or her drawing paper. *The first thing Richard does is say hello to his dog, so he will draw that in the first section on his paper.*

## Discussing Problem 2

Observing the children as they work and discussing their stories will give me a chance to assess their thinking.

To prompt the children to use the ordinals I will say, *Show me the first, second, third, fourth, and fifth thing you do at home to get ready for school.* When all the children have finished, I will ask for volunteers to share their drawings and tell the class about them. This is another opportunity for the children to communicate their thinking. If they are not using the ordinal numbers at all as they describe their pictures, I will interject them. I could say, *So, the **fourth** thing you do is eat your breakfast.* To check to see if they are understanding the ordinals I'll ask, *Why did Mario use first, second, third, fourth, fifth and not one, two, three, four, five?*

## Problem 3

Now would be a good time to play a game of *Simon Says*, which will provide another opportunity for me to assess how the children are understanding the ordinals. I could call children up to the front of the room in groups of five. Both the *Simon Says* players and the observers could participate.

## Discussing Problem 3

When a group of five children is standing at the front of the room, I need to make sure the children are all thinking of the same person when I call out ordinal numbers. I could indicate one child to be the beginning of the line.

I'll instruct them to count off by ones, which will again help the children connect the cardinals to the ordinals. Then I could give specific instructions to the players. *Both the first and fourth person should hop on one foot.* I can involve the observers by asking such questions as, *Who is second in line?*

## Reviewing the Plan

Before teaching this lesson, I want to make sure that it meets my objective and uses the process skills effectively. My objective is for the children to begin to learn the ordinal numbers. Communication and representation are at the center of both the stories and *Simon Says*. If they understand the ordinal concept, they should be able to apply the ordinal numbers. Tomorrow I will continue the work with ordinals by having them make lines using objects and having them follow directions with ordinals and give directions as well.